Glory to God

New music for the Mass

edited by

Peter Jones & Alan Smith

Decani Music

Glory to God
New music for the Mass

Decani Music, Oak House, 70 High Street, Brandon, Suffolk IP27 0AU
www.decanimusic.co.uk

The musical settings of excerpts from the English translation of *The Roman Missal* are published with the approval of the Department for Christian Life and Worship of the Catholic Bishops' Conference of England and Wales.

ISBN 978-1-900314-21-3

Printed by Hobbs the Printers Ltd, Totton, Southampton

Editors – Peter Jones and Alan Smith
Editorial assistance – Keith Ainsworth
Typesetting and music engraving – Alan Smith
Cover Art – Church of The Sacred Heart and St Margaret Mary, Birmingham (mosaic)

We are grateful to all those composers, authors and copyright holders who have allowed their music and texts to be used in this work. We have made strenuous attempts to trace all applicable copyright holders and believe that we have appropriate permission where necessary. We are sorry if we have inadvertently breached copyright and will take all reasonable steps to rectify the position in future editions if notified.

FOREWORD

Psalm 95 begins with a spirited command: 'O sing a new song to the Lord.'

Alongside the introduction of the new English translation of the Roman Missal in the year 2011, there is a need, a desire and a longing for such 'new song'. Indeed, our Bishops are offering renewed encouragement to pray the Mass in song, for it is song that permits those who sing to enter ever more deeply into the sacred mysteries we celebrate. Those who sing well do indeed pray twice.

Glory to God is a deliberately eclectic collection of liturgical music of our own day, composed to facilitate the sung prayer of the People of God. We, the editors, hope that these settings of the newly-translated texts will both help and stimulate the active participation of the faithful in the celebration of the Mass: externally, through vocal expression, and internally, through implanting the words of the liturgy in the hearts and minds of the singers.

'Let us rejoice and exult and give him the glory.' (Rev 19:7)

Peter Jones
Alan Smith

TABLE OF CONTENTS

FULL SETTINGS OF THE MASS

Eucharistic Acclamations

Settings of other sections of the Mass

A Parish Mass

Lord, have mercy

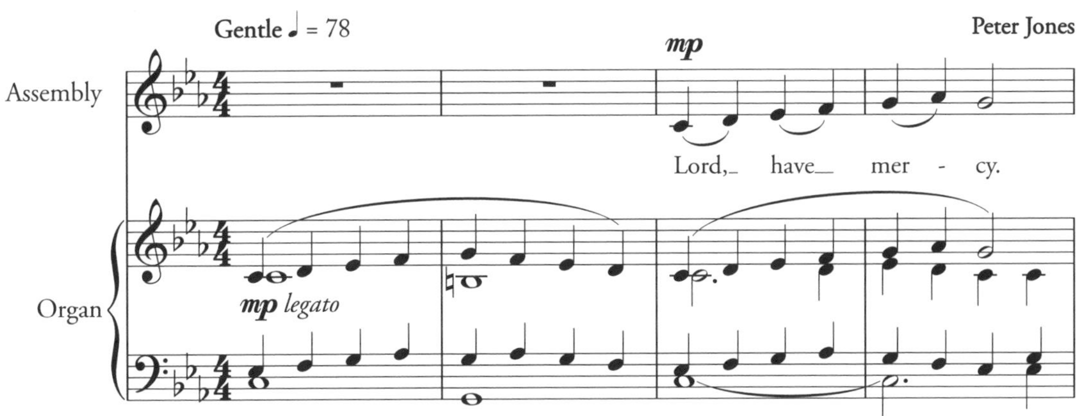

Gentle ♩ = 78
Peter Jones
mp
Assembly
Lord, have mer - cy.
Organ
mp legato

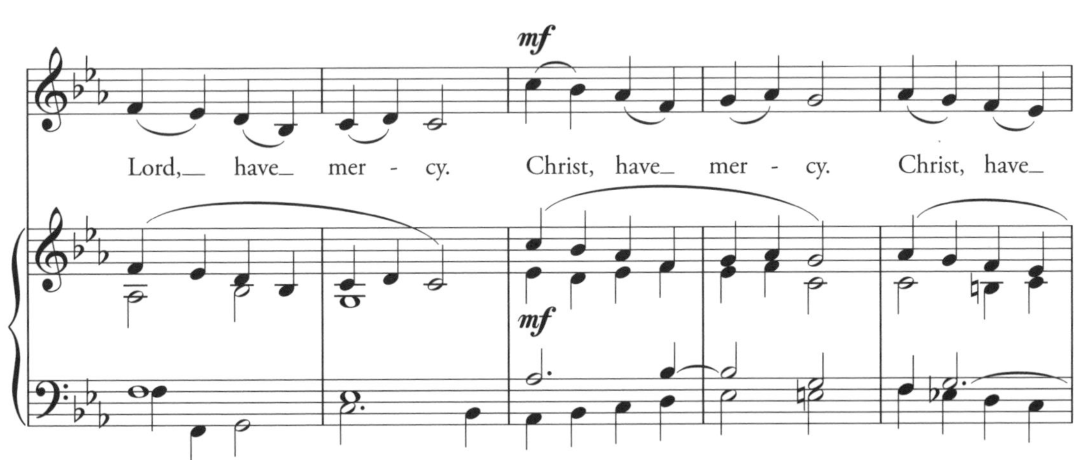

mf
Lord, have mer - cy. Christ, have mer - cy. Christ, have
mf

mp
mer - cy. Lord, have mer - cy. Lord, have mer - cy.
mp

A Parish Mass

Penitential Act with Invocations

Peter Jones

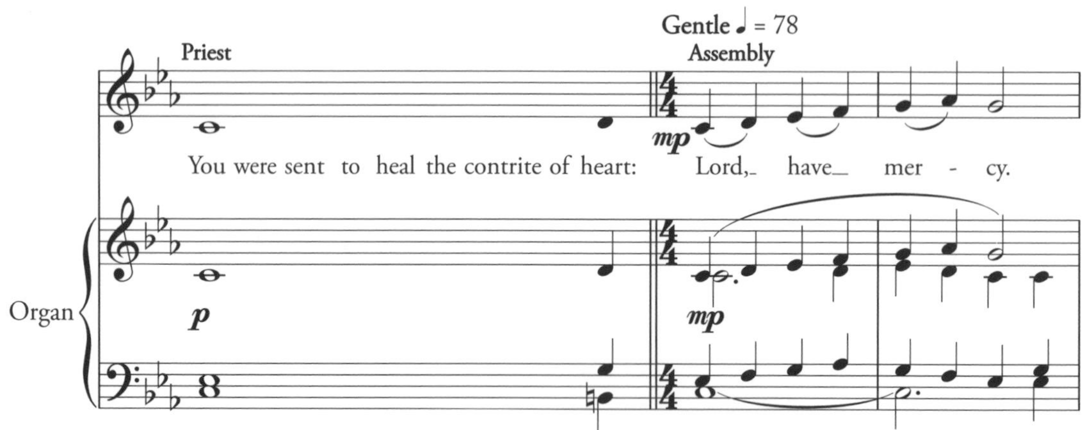

Gentle ♩ = 78
Priest
Assembly
mp
You were sent to heal the contrite of heart: Lord, have mer - cy.
Organ
p
mp

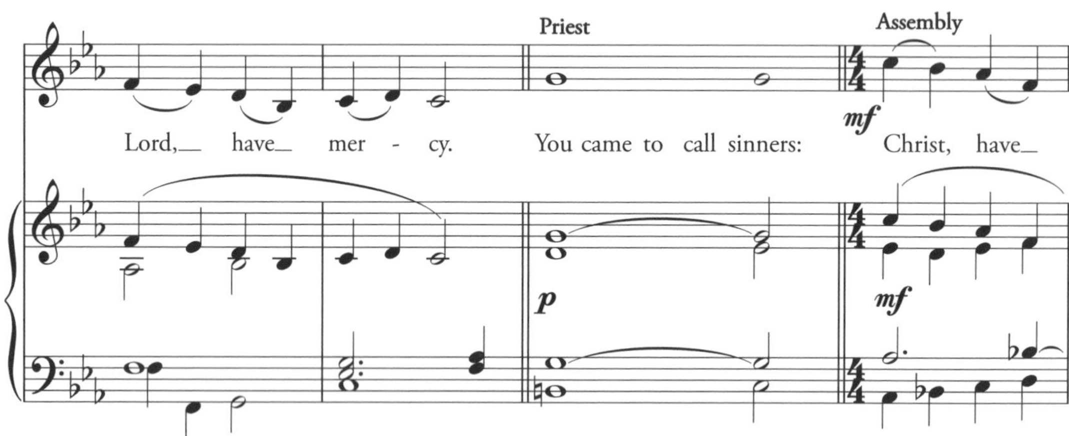

Priest
Assembly
mf
Lord, have mer - cy. You came to call sinners: Christ, have
p
mf

Priest
mer - cy. Christ, have mer - cy. You are seated at the
p

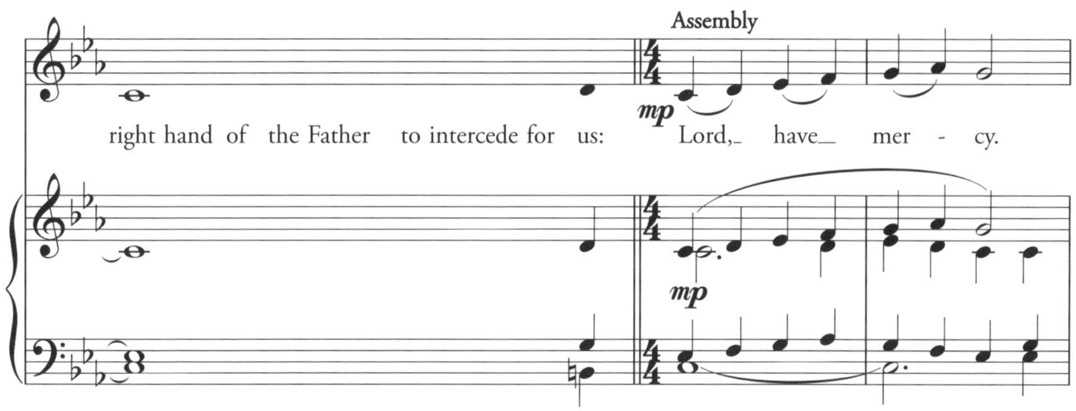
Assembly
right hand of the Father to intercede for us: Lord,_ have_ mer - cy.
mp

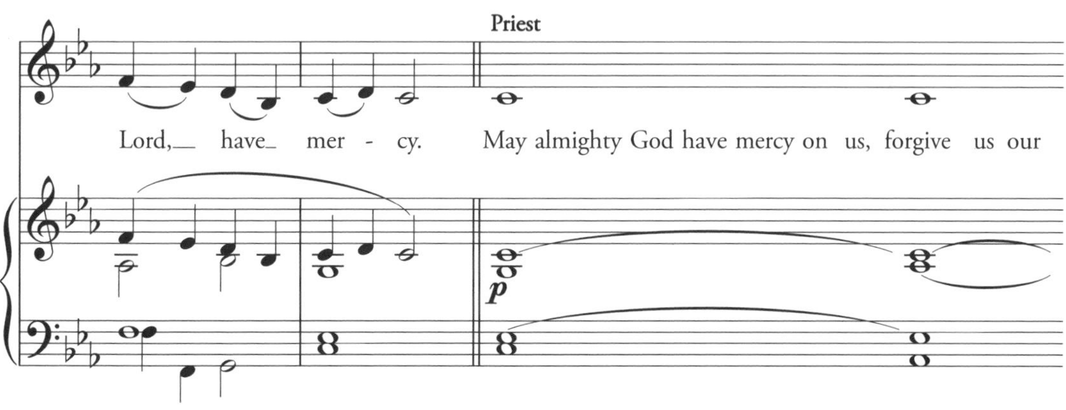
Priest
Lord,_ have_ mer - cy. May almighty God have mercy on us, forgive us our
p

Assembly
sins, and bring us to ev - er - last - ing life. A - men.
mp

A Parish Mass

Glory to God

Peter Jones

Steady ♩ = c.90
Assembly
Organ
mf
Glo-ry to God in the high-est, and on
earth peace to peo-ple of good will. We praise you, we bless you, we a-
dore you, we glo-ri-fy you, we give you thanks for your great glo-ry,

f
Lord God, hea-ven-ly King, O God, al-might - y Fa - ther.
f
mp

p
Lord Je - sus Christ, On - ly Be-got-ten Son,
p legato

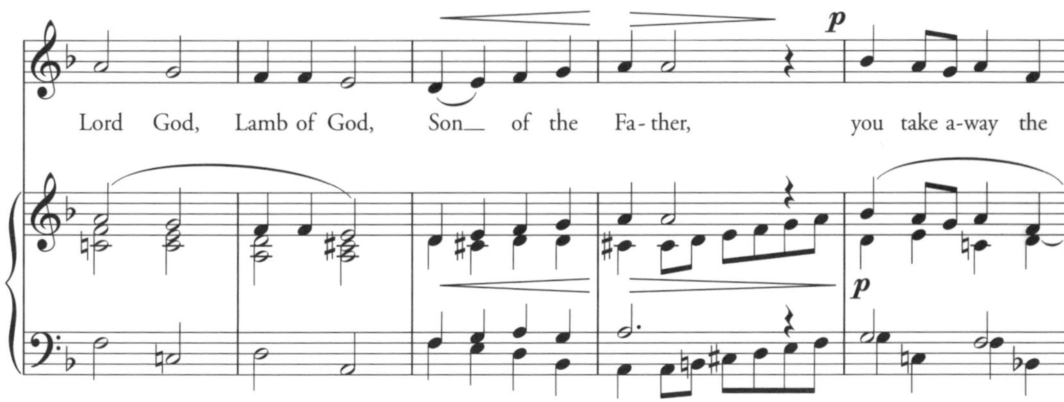
p
Lord God, Lamb of God, Son of the Fa - ther, you take a-way the
p

mp
sins of the world, have mer - cy on us; you take a-way the
mp

mf
sins of the world, re - ceive_ our prayer; you are seat-ed at the
mf

poco rit. - - - - - A tempo
f
right hand of the Fa- ther, have mer-cy on us.
f
mf

mf
For you a-lone are the Ho-ly One, you a - lone are the

Lord, you a - lone are the Most High, Je - sus Christ, with the Ho - ly
f
mf
f

rit.
Spi - rit, in the glo - ry of God the Fa - ther. A - men.

A Parish Mass

Holy, Holy, Holy

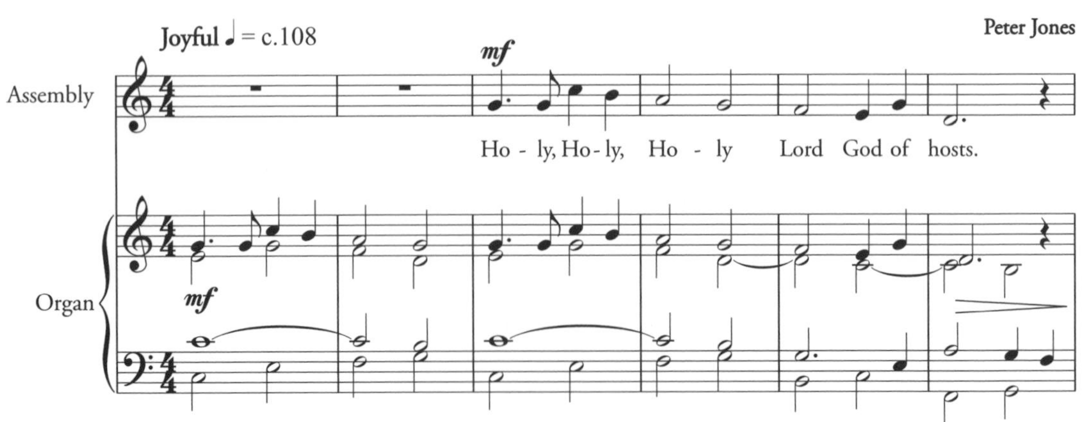
Joyful ♩ = c.108
Peter Jones
Assembly
Organ
mf
Ho - ly, Ho - ly, Ho - ly Lord God of hosts.

mp
f
Heav'n and earth, heav'n and earth are full of your glo - ry. Ho - san - na in the high - est.

mf
f
Bless'd is he who comes in the name of the Lord. Ho - san - na in the high - est.

A Parish Mass

We proclaim your Death

Peter Jones

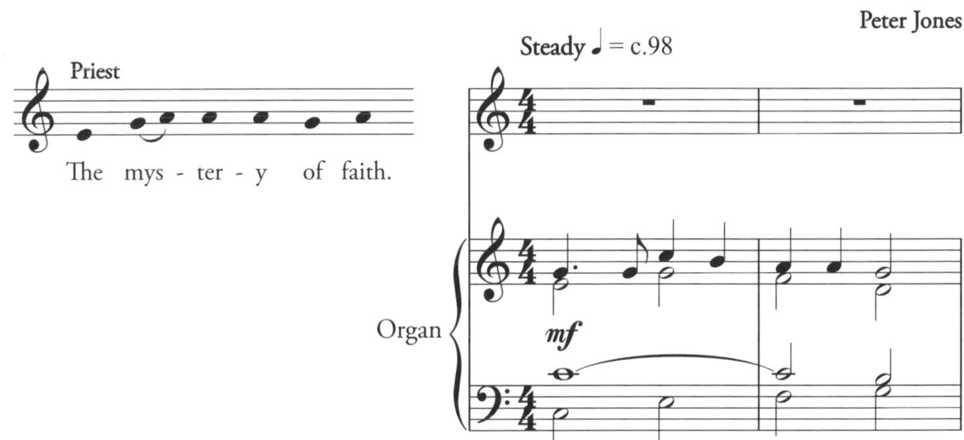
Steady ♩ = c.98
Priest
The mys - ter - y of faith.
Organ
mf

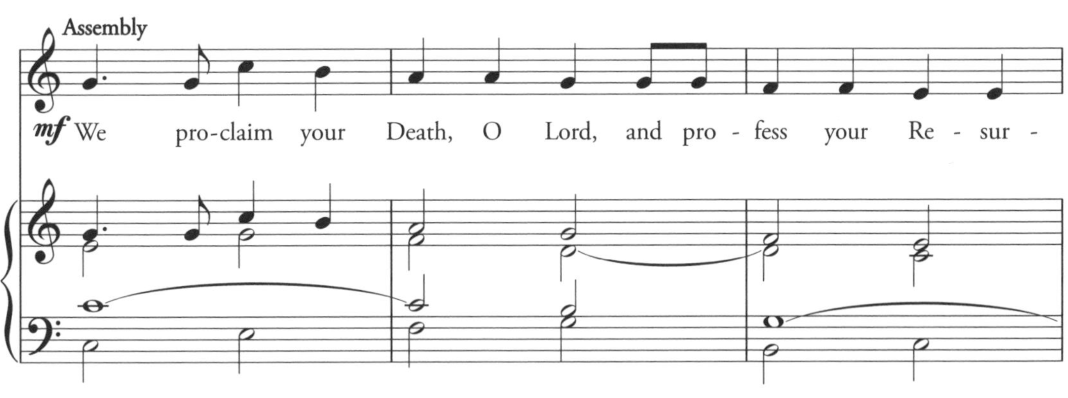
Assembly
mf We pro-claim your Death, O Lord, and pro - fess your Re - sur -

rec - tion un - til you come a - gain.

A Parish Mass

When we eat this Bread

Peter Jones

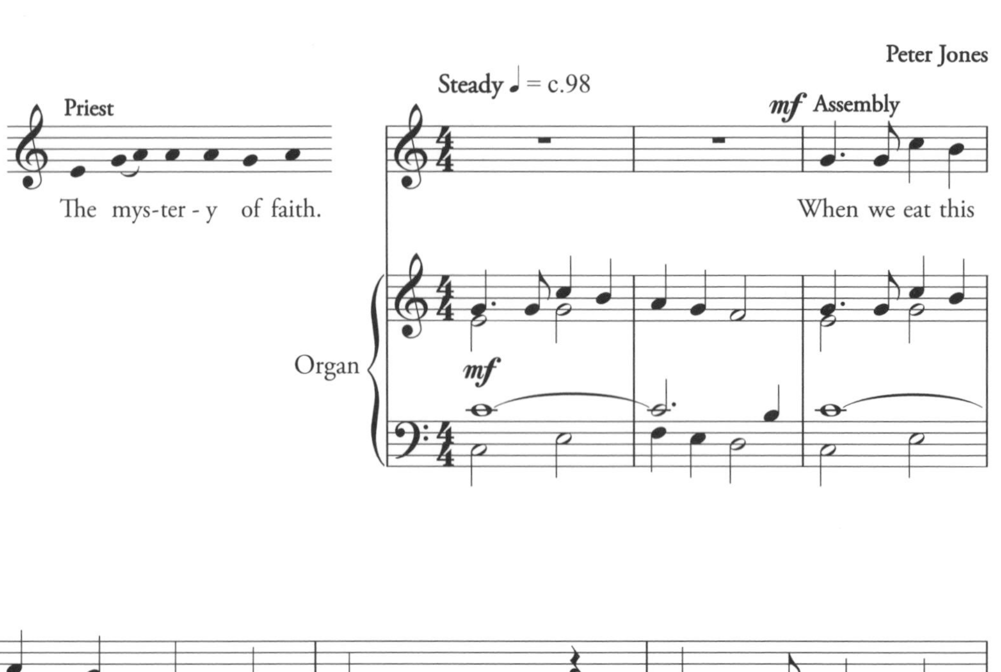
Steady ♩ = c.98
Priest
The mys-ter - y of faith.
mf Assembly
When we eat this
Organ
mf

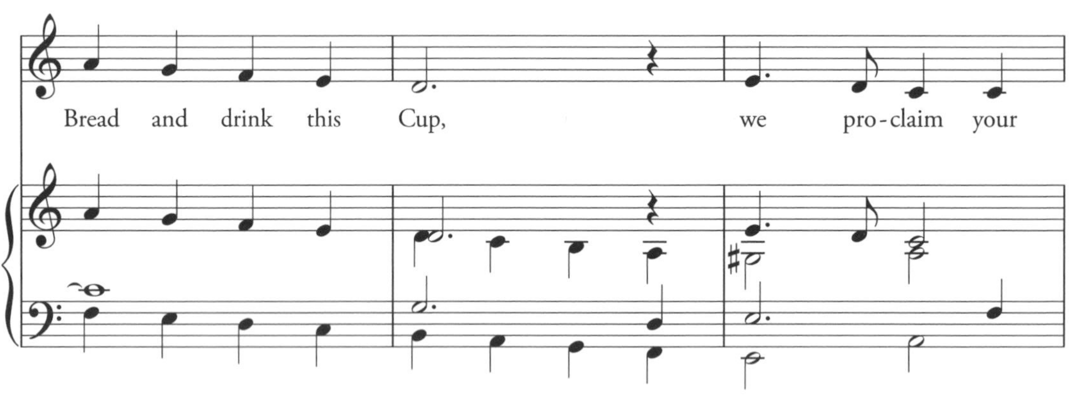
Bread and drink this Cup, we pro-claim your

Death, O Lord, un - til you come a - gain.

A Parish Mass

Save us, Saviour of the world

Peter Jones

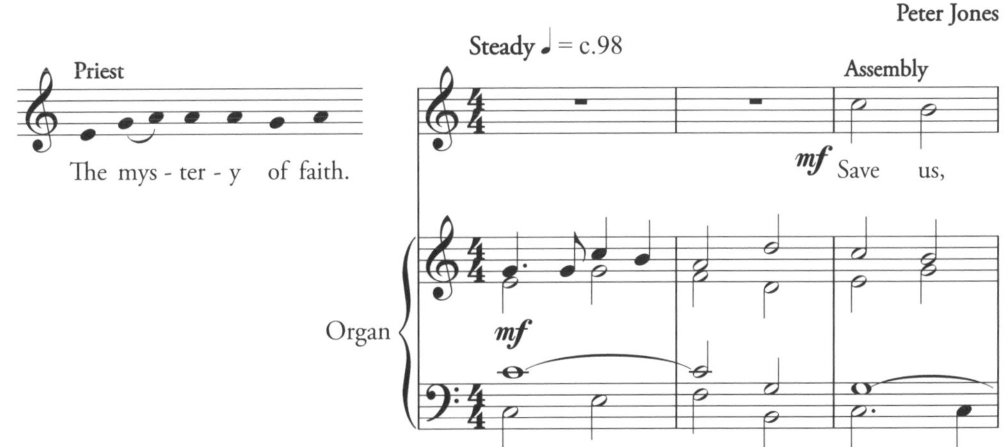
Steady ♩ = c.98
Priest
The mys - ter - y of faith.
Assembly
mf Save us,
Organ
mf

save us, Sav - iour of the world, for by your

Cross and Re - sur - rec - tion you have set us free.

A Parish Mass

Amen

Peter Jones

Priest *(Missal chant)*

Through him ...

Steady ♩ = c.98

Organ

mf

Assembly

mf A - men, a - men, a - men, a - - - men.

A Parish Mass

Lamb of God

Peter Jones

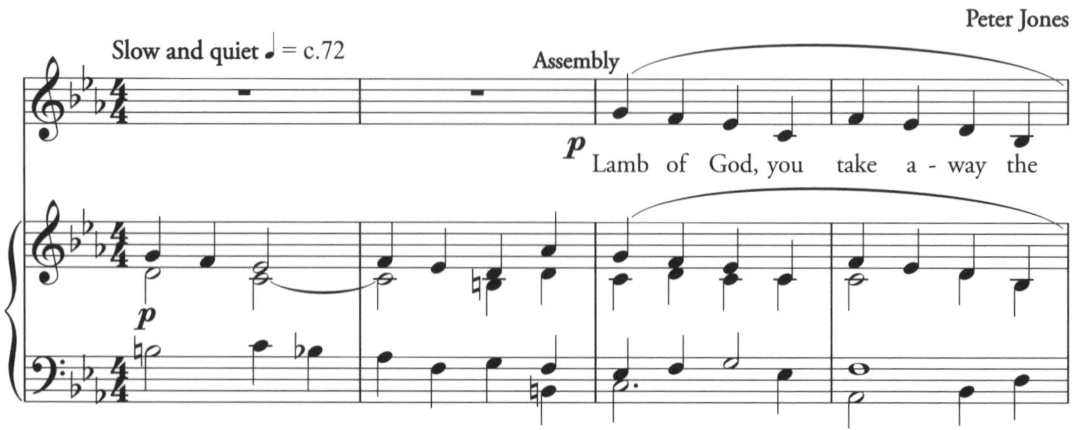
Slow and quiet ♩ = c.72
Assembly
p Lamb of God, you take a - way the
p

sins of the world, have mer-cy on us.
mp
Lamb of God, you take a-way the
mp

sins of the world, have mer-cy on us.
p
Lamb of God, you
p

pp
take a-way the sins of the world, grant us peace.
pp

Belmont Mass

Penitential Act with Invocations

Christopher Walker

Priest
Cantor
Assembly
You were sent to heal the con-trite of heart: Ky-ri-e, e-le-i-son. Ky-ri-e, e-le-i-son.
Lord, have mer-cy. Lord, have mer-cy.
Em Am6/E Em Am Em C D Am
p
mp

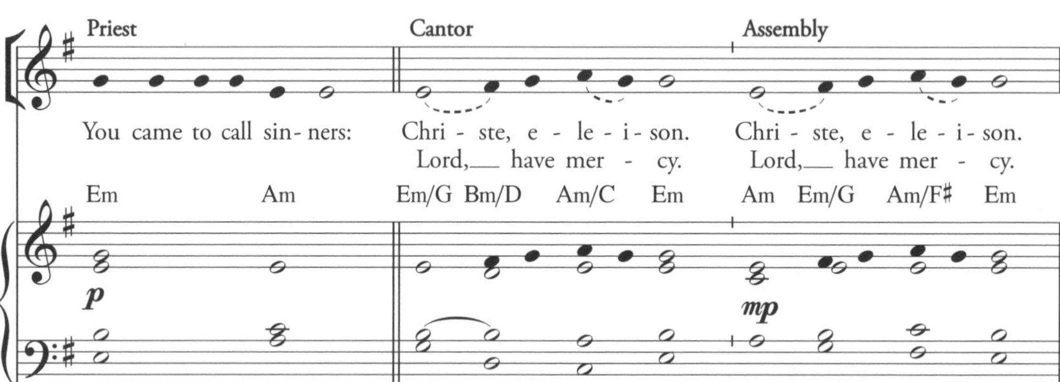
Priest
Cantor
Assembly
You came to call sin-ners: Chri-ste, e-le-i-son. Chri-ste, e-le-i-son.
Lord, have mer-cy. Lord, have mer-cy.
Em Am Em/G Bm/D Am/C Em Am Em/G Am/F♯ Em
p
mp

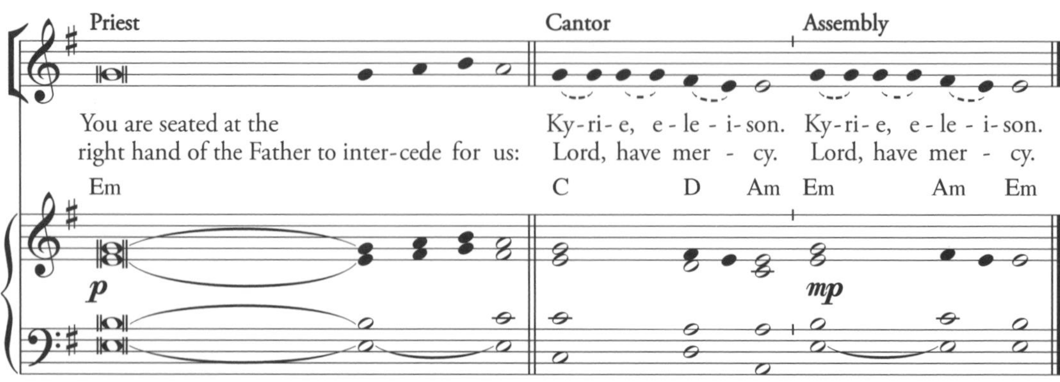
Priest
Cantor
Assembly
You are seated at the
right hand of the Father to inter-cede for us: Ky-ri-e, e-le-i-son. Ky-ri-e, e-le-i-son.
Lord, have mer-cy. Lord, have mer-cy.
Em C D Am Em Am Em
p
mp

BELMONT MASS

Glory to God

Christopher Walker

Assembly
mf chant in speech rhythm
Glory to God in the highest, and on earth peace to peo-ple of good will.
G D Am/C G
mf
We praise you, we bless you, we a-dore you, we glorify you, we give you thanks for your great glory,
Em Am/C D C/E G
Lord God, heav - en - ly King, O God, al - might - y Father.
C G/B D G
Lord Jesus Christ, Only Be-got-ten Son, Lord God, Lamb of God, Son of the Father,
Em Am/C D Am/C Em

p
you take away the sins of the world, have mer - cy on us;
C Em D G
p
mp
you take away the sins of the world, re - ceive our prayer;
Bm Am/C C/E G
mp
you are seated at the right hand of the Father, have mer - cy on us.
C G/B D B
mf
For you a - lone are the Holy One, you a - lone are the Lord,
Em Am/C D C/E G
mf

you alone are the Most High, Je - sus Christ, with the Ho - ly Spirit,
C G/B D B
rall. e cresc.
in the glory of God the Father. A - men, a - men.
Cmaj7 Am D Em Cmaj7 C6 G
rall. e cresc.

Gospel Acclamation

Christopher Walker

Cantor 1st time, then Assembly

Fine

Al - le - lu - ia, al - le - lu - ia, al - le - lu - ia.

Al - le - lu - ia, al - le - lu - ia, al - le - lu - ia.

Al - le - lu - ia, al - le - lu - ia, al - le - lu - ia.

Fine

VERSES

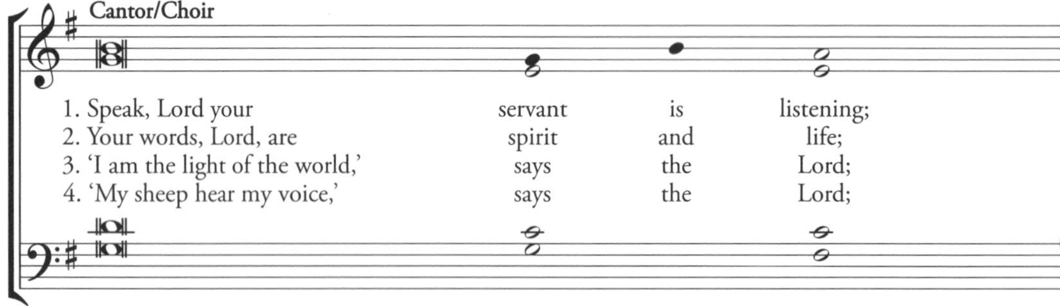
Cantor/Choir
1. Speak, Lord your servant is listening;
2. Your words, Lord, are spirit and life;
3. 'I am the light of the world,' says the Lord;
4. 'My sheep hear my voice,' says the Lord;

D.C.
1. you have the words of ever - last - - ing life.
2. you have the words of ever - last - - ing life.
3. 'whoever follows me will have the light___ of life.'
4. 'I know them, and they fol - - low me.'

Lenten Gospel Acclamation

Christopher Walker

Cantor/Choir 1st time, then Assembly
Fine
Praise and hon-our to you, Lord_ Je - sus Christ!
Praise and hon-our to you, Lord_ Je - sus Christ!
Praise and hon-our to you, Lord_ Je - sus Christ!
Praise and hon-our to you, Lord_ Je - sus Christ!
mf
Fine
VERSES (Year A)
Cantor/Choir
1. We do not live on bread a - lone,
2. From the bright cloud the Father's voice is heard:
3. Lord, you are really the Saviour of the world;
4. 'I am the light of the world,' says the Lord;
5. 'I am the resurrection and the life,' says the Lord;

D.S.

1. but on every word that comes from the mouth of God.
2. 'This is my Son, the Be - lovèd. Listen to him.'
3. give me the living water, that I may never get thirsty.
4. 'anyone who follows me will have the light of life.'
5. 'whoever believes in me will nev - - er die.'

BELMONT MASS

Holy, Holy, Holy

Christopher Walker

Assembly
mf Ho-ly, Ho - ly, Ho - ly Lord God of hosts.
G Am D G Am D Bm Am/C D
mp
mf
Heav-en and earth are full of your glory. Ho - san - na in the high-est.
Am Fmaj7 Dm7 Em Am/C C D
mp Bless - ed is he who comes in the name of the Lord.
G Em Am/C Bm Am/C D
mp
Ho - san - na in the high-est, ho - san - na in the high - est.
Am/C Em Am/C C Gsus4 G

BELMONT MASS

We proclaim your Death

Christopher Walker

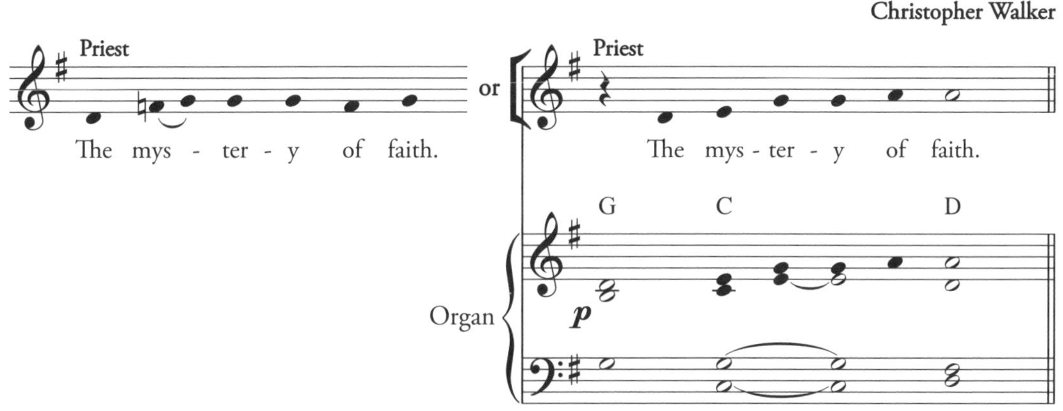
Priest
The mys - ter - y of faith.
or
Priest
The mys - ter - y of faith.
G C D
Organ
p

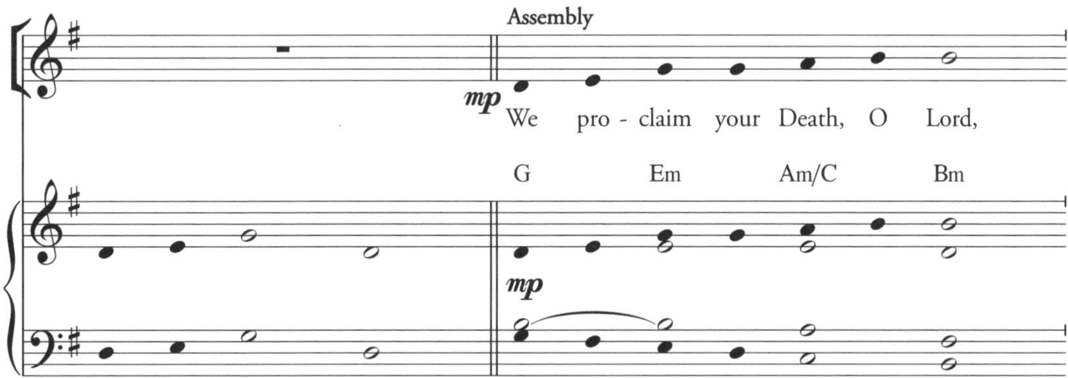
Assembly
mp
We pro - claim your Death, O Lord,
G Em Am/C Bm
mp

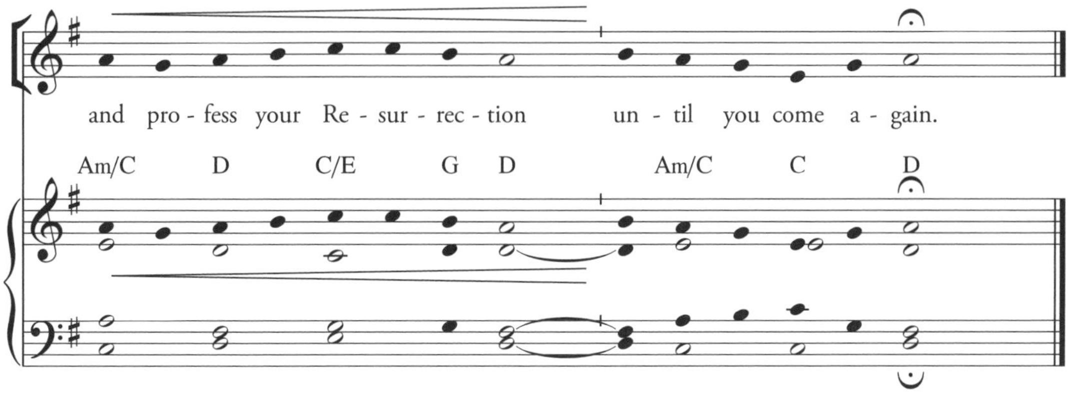
and pro - fess your Re - sur - rec - tion un - til you come a - gain.
Am/C D C/E G D Am/C C D

BELMONT MASS

When we eat this Bread

Christopher Walker

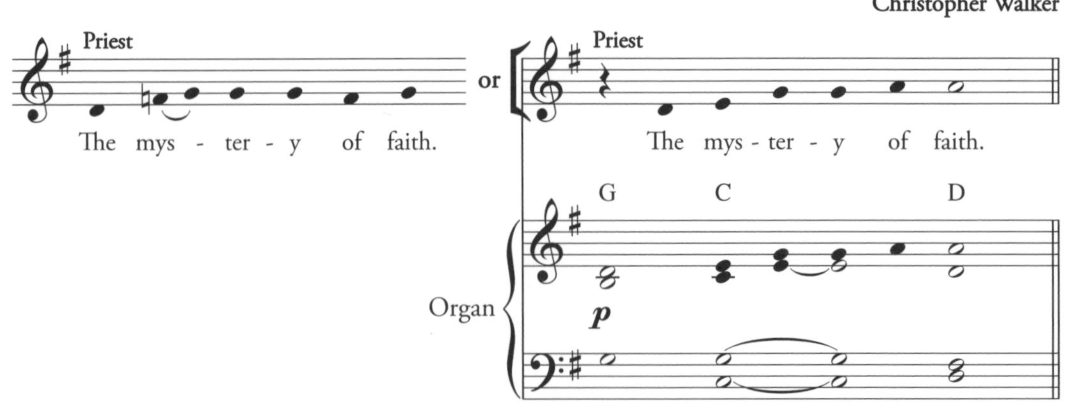
Priest
The mys - ter - y of faith.
or
Priest
The mys - ter - y of faith.
G
C
D
Organ
p

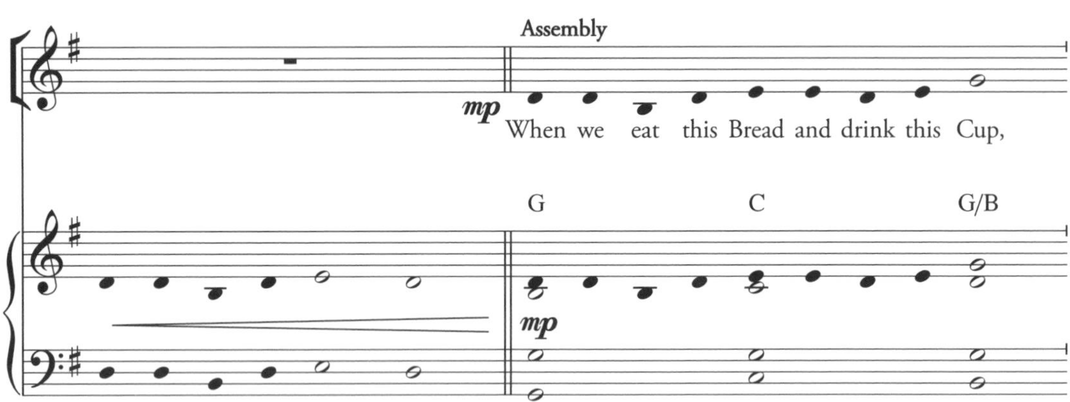
Assembly
mp
When we eat this Bread and drink this Cup,
G
C
G/B
mp

we pro - claim your Death, O Lord, un - til you come a - gain.
Em
D
Am/C
Bm
Em

BELMONT MASS

Save us, Saviour of the world

Christopher Walker

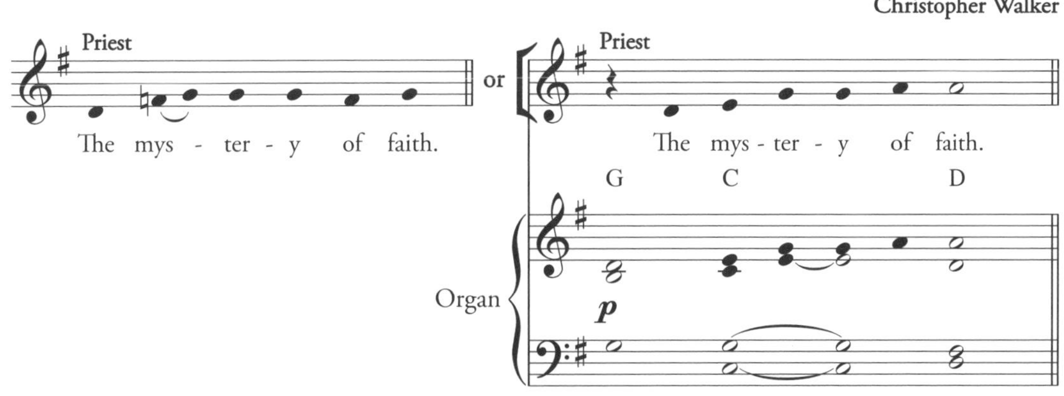
Priest
The mys - ter - y of faith.
or
Priest
The mys - ter - y of faith.
G C D
Organ
p

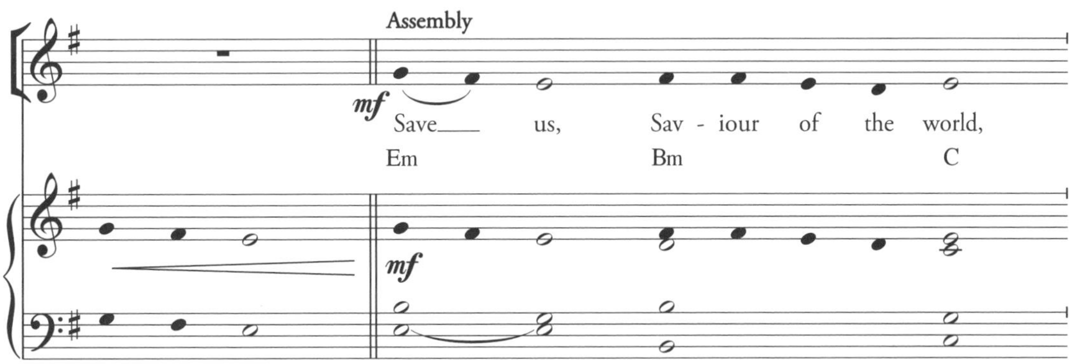
Assembly
mf
Save us, Sav - iour of the world,
Em Bm C
mf

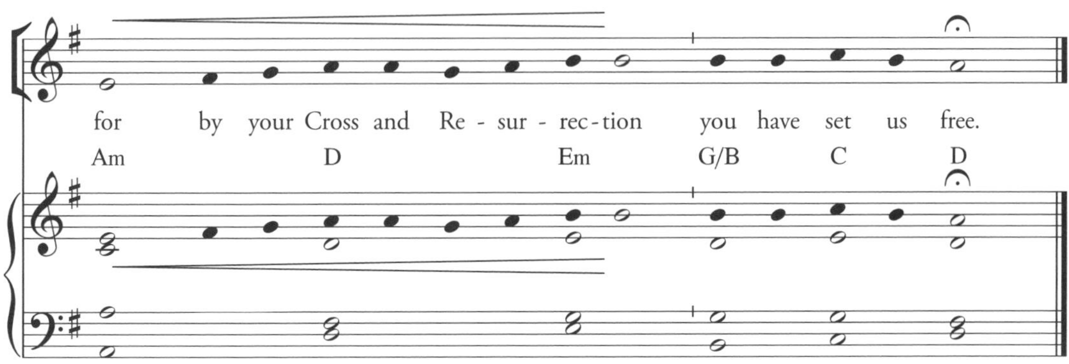
for by your Cross and Re - sur - rec - tion you have set us free.
Am D Em G/B C D

BELMONT MASS

Doxology and Amen

Christopher Walker

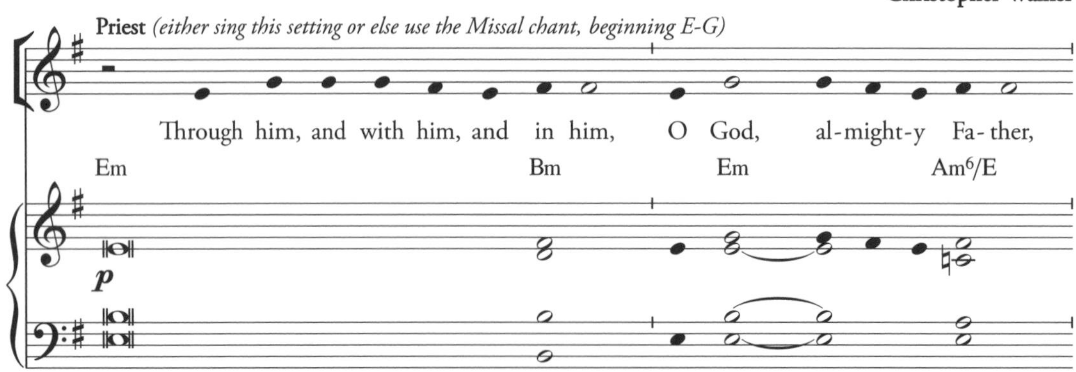
Priest (either sing this setting or else use the Missal chant, beginning E-G)
Through him, and with him, and in him, O God, al-might-y Fa- ther,
Em
Bm
Em
Am6/E
p

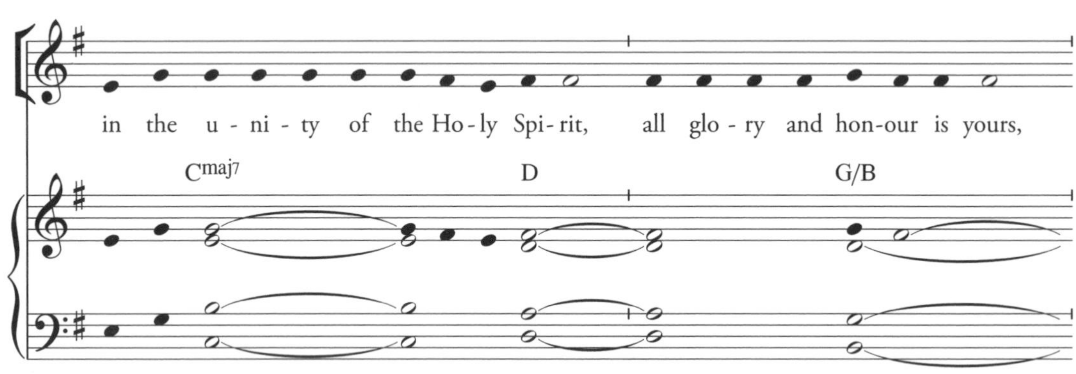
in the u - ni - ty of the Ho - ly Spi - rit, all glo - ry and hon-our is yours,
Cmaj7
D
G/B

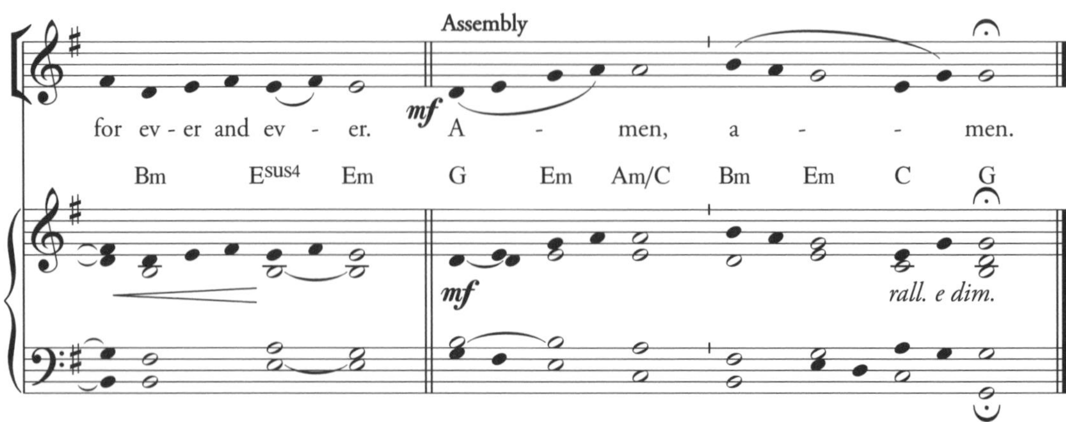
Assembly
for ev - er and ev - er.
mf
A - men, a - - men.
Bm
Esus4
Em
G
Em
Am/C
Bm
Em
C
G
mf
rall. e dim.

BELMONT MASS

The Lord's Prayer

Christopher Walker

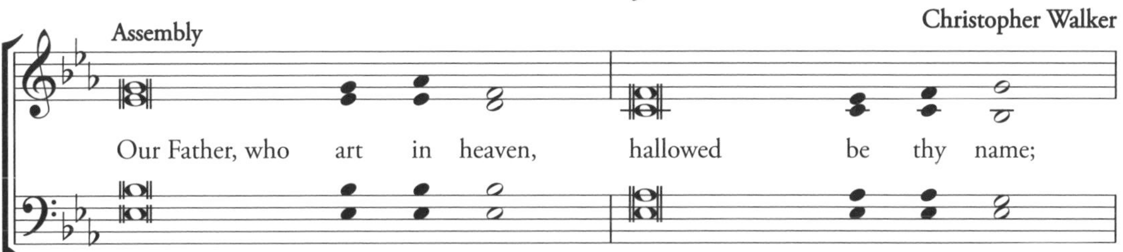
Assembly
Our Father, who art in heaven, hallowed be thy name;

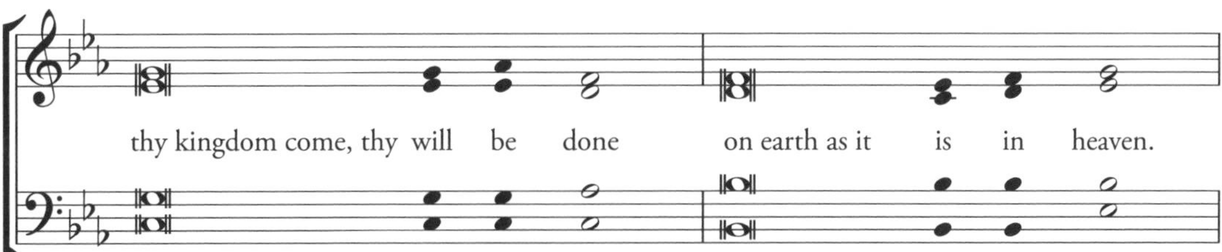
thy kingdom come, thy will be done on earth as it is in heaven.

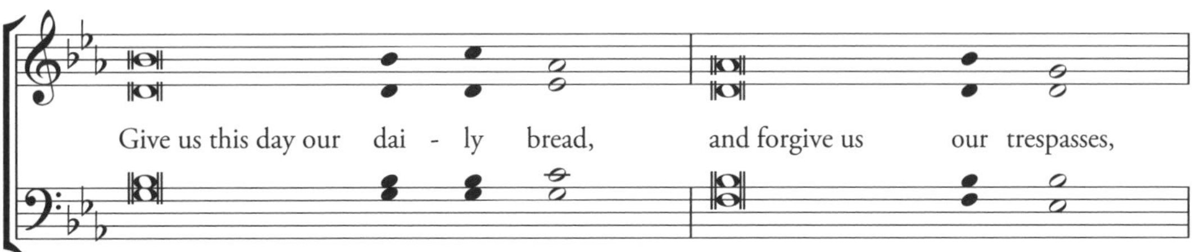
Give us this day our dai - ly bread, and forgive us our trespasses,

as we for - give those who trespass a - gainst us;

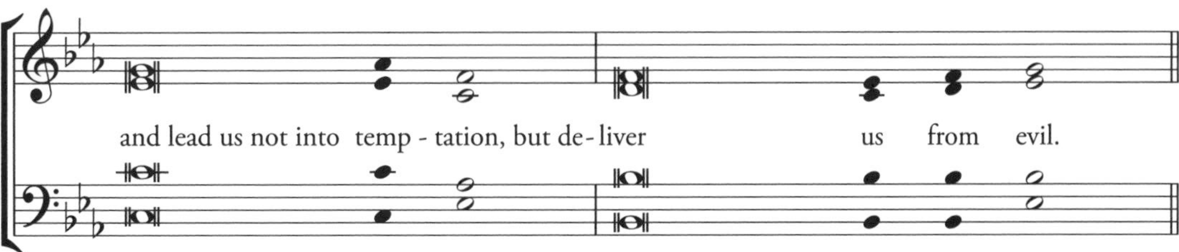
and lead us not into temp - tation, but de - liver us from evil.

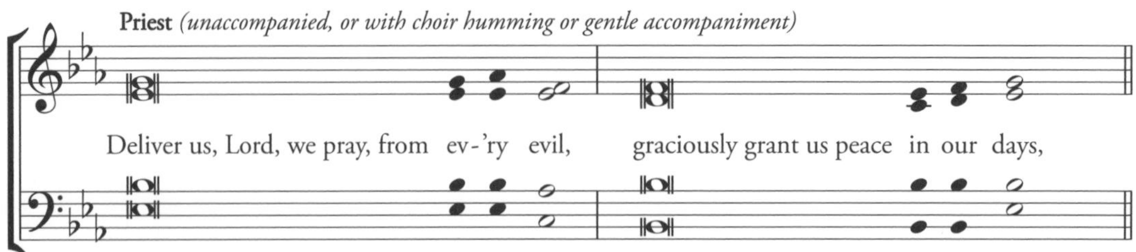
Priest (unaccompanied, or with choir humming or gentle accompaniment)
Deliver us, Lord, we pray, from ev-'ry evil,
graciously grant us peace in our days,

that, by the help of your mercy, we may be always free from sin

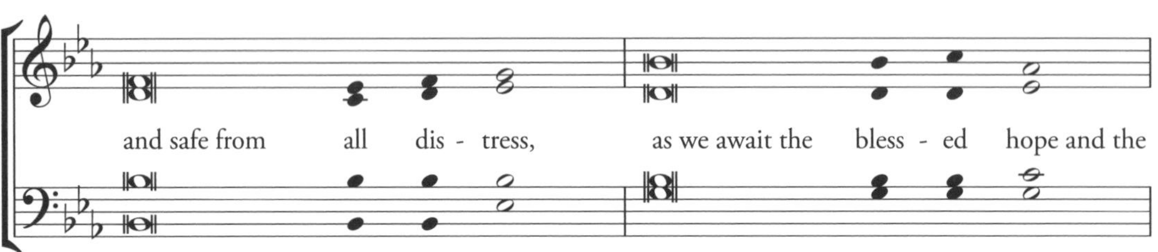
and safe from all dis - tress,
as we await the bless - ed hope and the

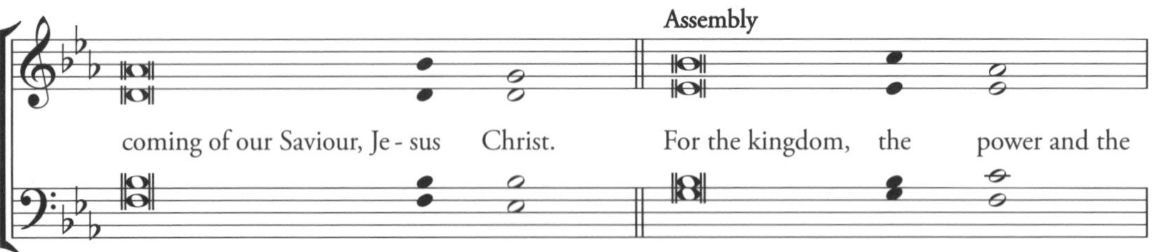
coming of our Saviour, Je - sus Christ.
Assembly
For the kingdom, the power and the

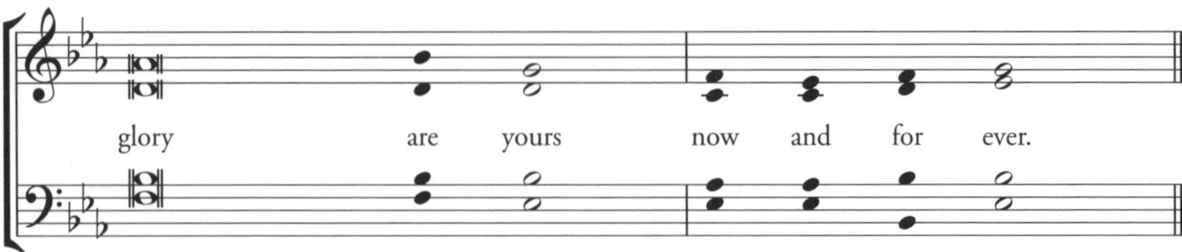
glory are yours now and for ever.

BELMONT MASS

Lamb of God

Christopher Walker

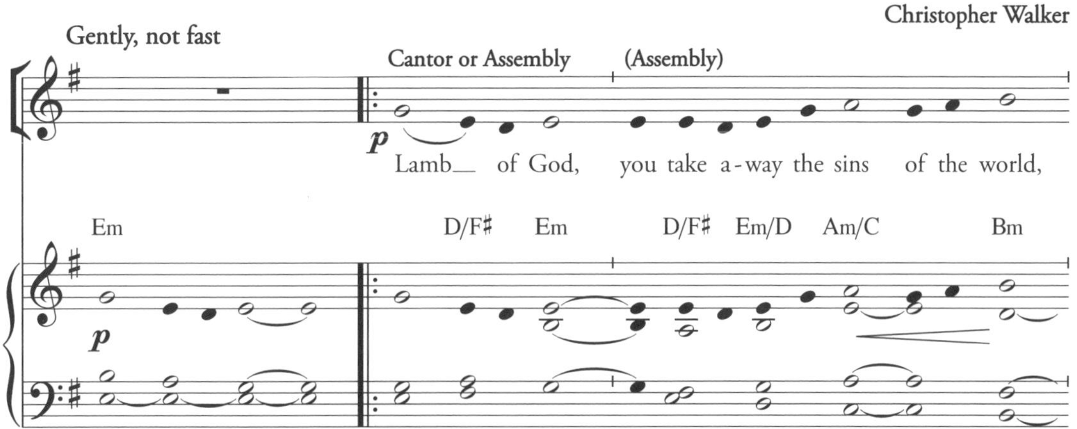
Gently, not fast
Cantor or Assembly
(Assembly)
p
Lamb__ of God, you take a-way the sins of the world,
Em
D/F♯
Em
D/F♯
Em/D
Am/C
Bm
p

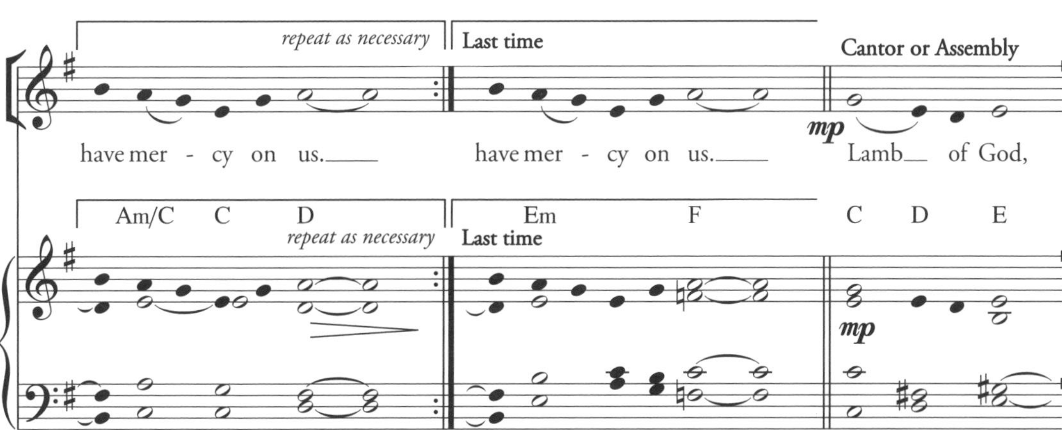
repeat as necessary
Last time
Cantor or Assembly
have mer - cy on us.__
have mer - cy on us.__
mp
Lamb__ of God,
Am/C
C
D
repeat as necessary
Last time
Em
F
C
D
E
mp

(Assembly)
you take a-way the sins of the world, grant us peace,__ grant us peace.
Am
Am6
B
Em
Em/D
Am/C
Am
Em*
rall. e dim.
(*E major ad libitum)

Mass of St Kenelm

Kyrie, eleison

Alan Smith

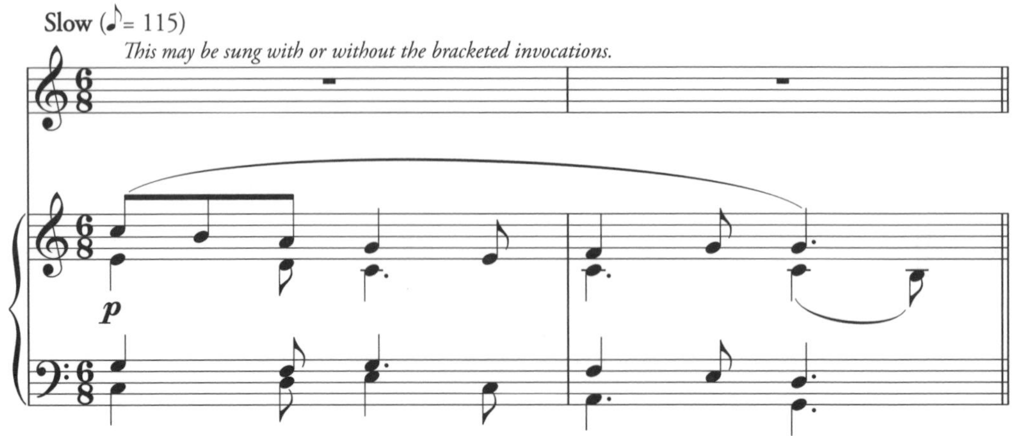
Slow (♪= 115)
This may be sung with or without the bracketed invocations.
p

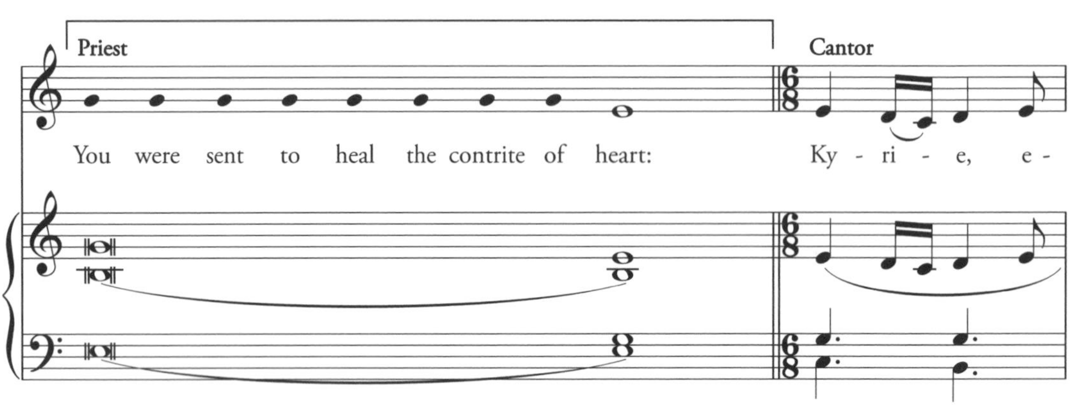
Priest
You were sent to heal the contrite of heart:
Cantor
Ky - ri - e, e -

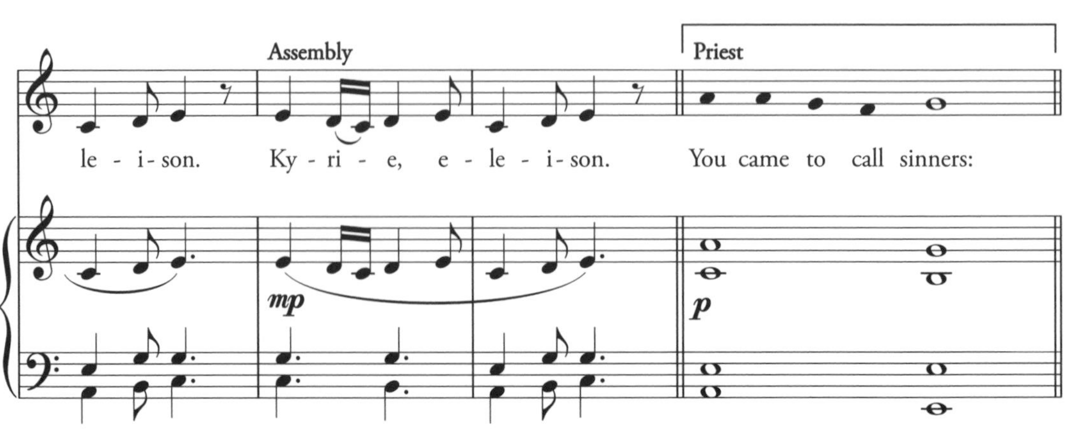
le - i - son.
Assembly
Ky - ri - e, e - le - i - son.
Priest
You came to call sinners:
mp
p

MASS OF ST KENELM (Kyrie, eleison)

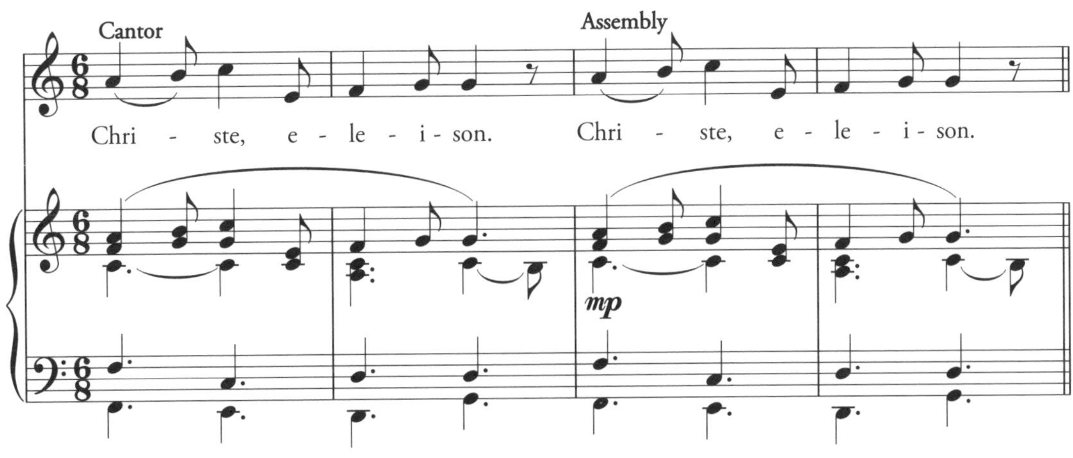
Cantor
Assembly
Chri - ste, e - le - i - son. Chri - ste, e - le - i - son.
mp

Priest
You are seated at the right hand of the Father to intercede for us:
p

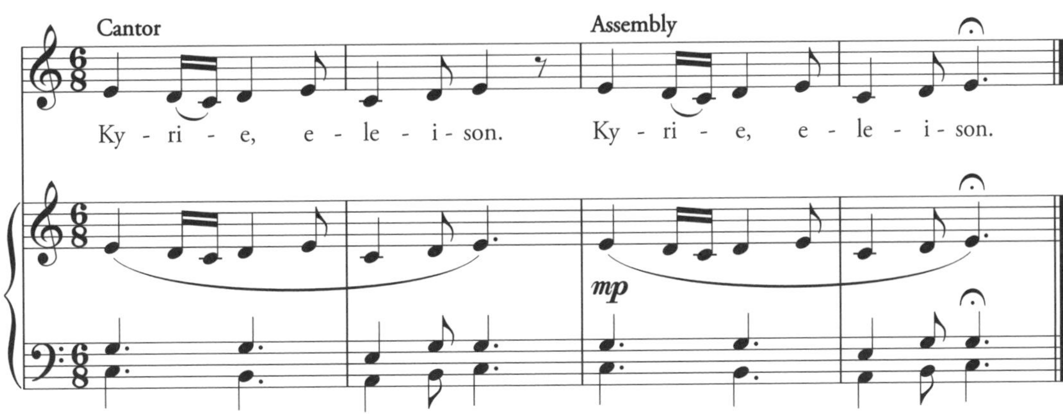
Cantor
Assembly
Ky - ri - e, e - le - i - son. Ky - ri - e, e - le - i - son.
mp

Mass of St Kenelm

Lord, have mercy

Alan Smith

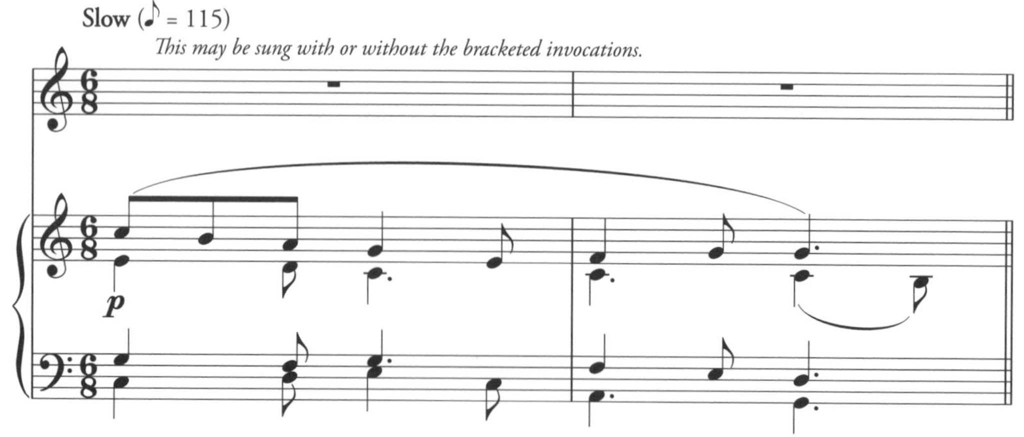
Slow (♪ = 115)
This may be sung with or without the bracketed invocations.
p

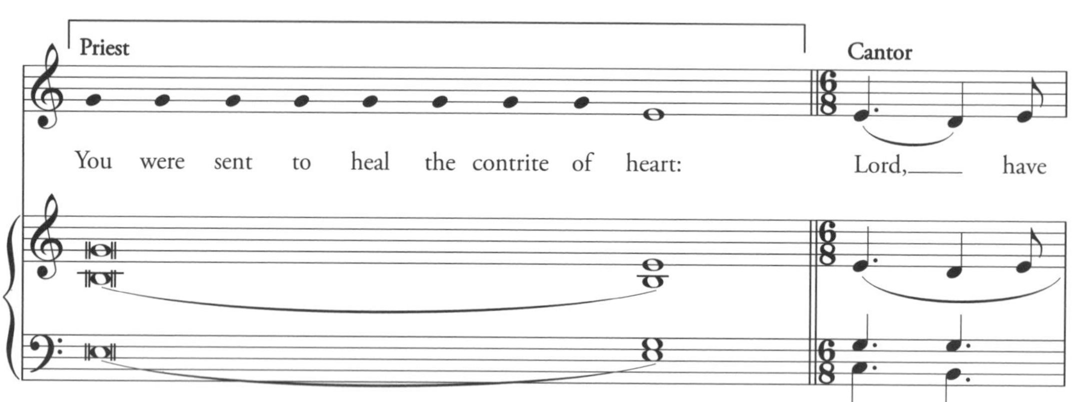
Priest
Cantor
You were sent to heal the contrite of heart:
Lord, have

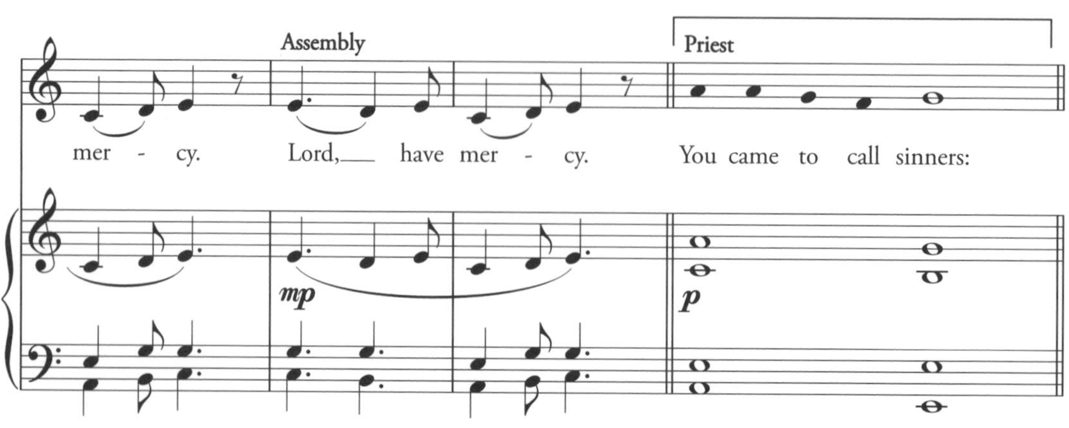
Assembly
Priest
mer - cy. Lord, have mer - cy.
You came to call sinners:
mp
p

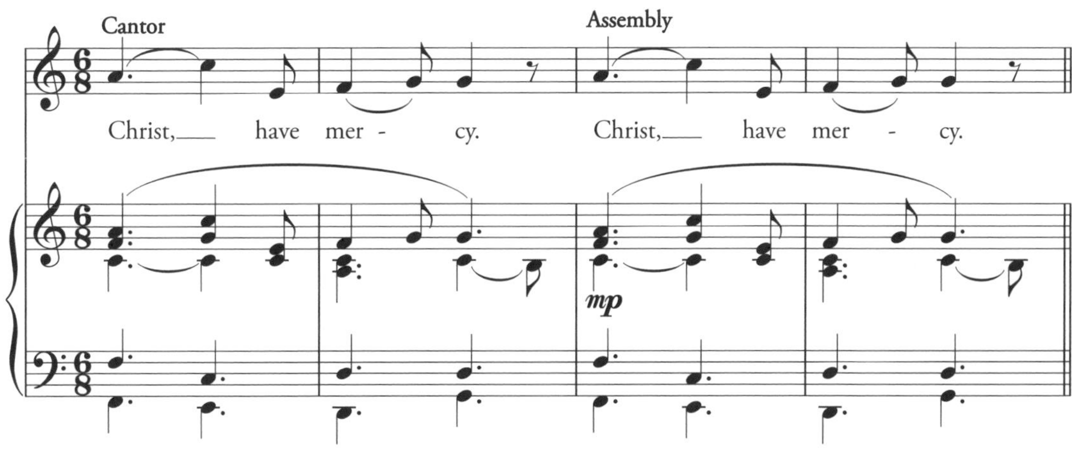
Cantor
Assembly
Christ, have mer - cy. Christ, have mer - cy.
mp

Priest
You are seated at the right hand of the Father to intercede for us:
p

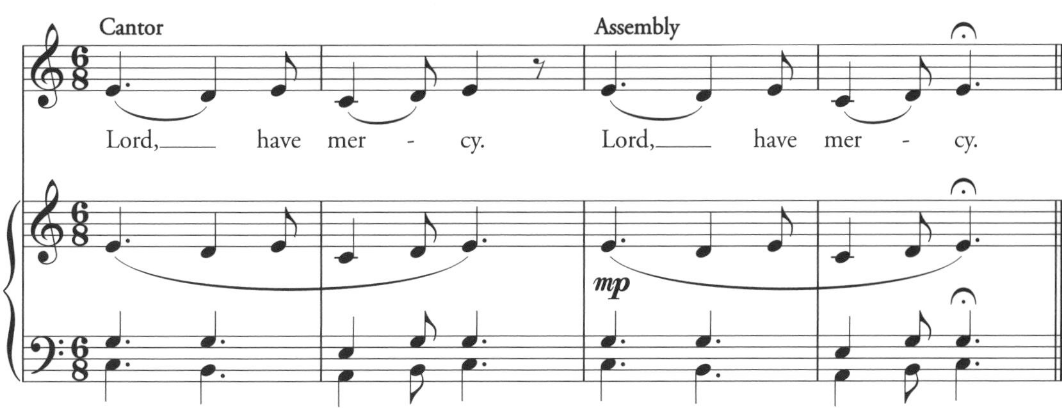
Cantor
Assembly
Lord, have mer - cy. Lord, have mer - cy.
mp

Mass of St Kenelm

Glory to God

Alan Smith

♩. = 60
* The priest or a cantor may intone the first phrase.
Assembly *
mf
Glo-ry to God in the
mf

high- est*, and on earth peace to peo-ple of good will.

We praise you, we bless you, we a - dore you, we

mp
glo-ri-fy you,
we give you thanks for your great glo-ry,
Lord_God,
mp

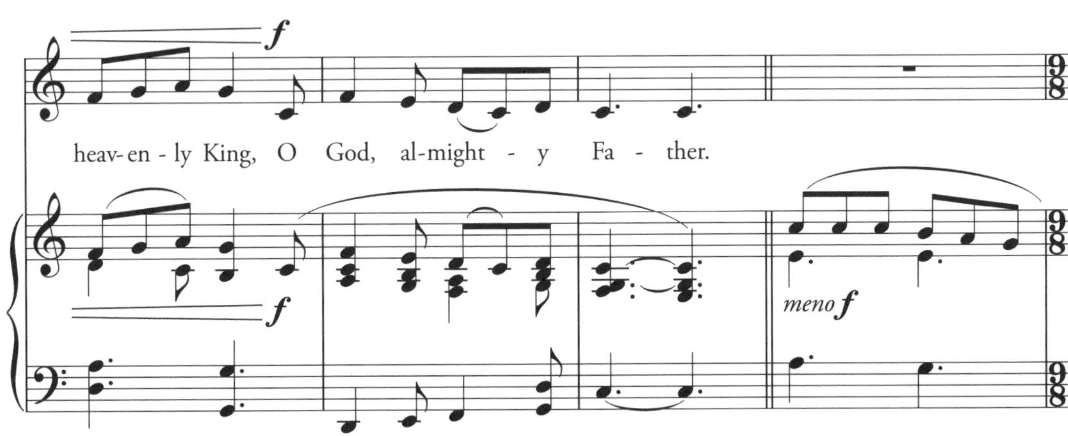
f
heav-en-ly King, O God, al-might - y Fa - ther.
f
meno f

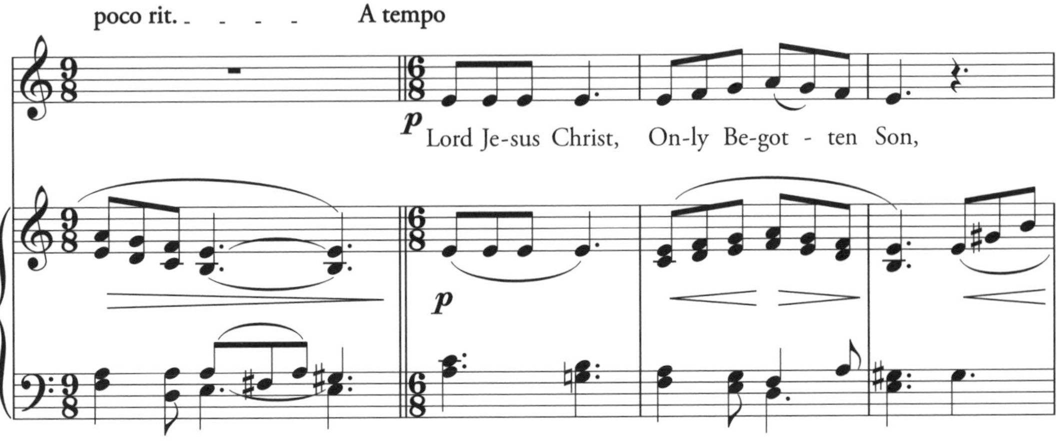
poco rit.
A tempo
p
Lord Je-sus Christ, On-ly Be-got - ten Son,
p

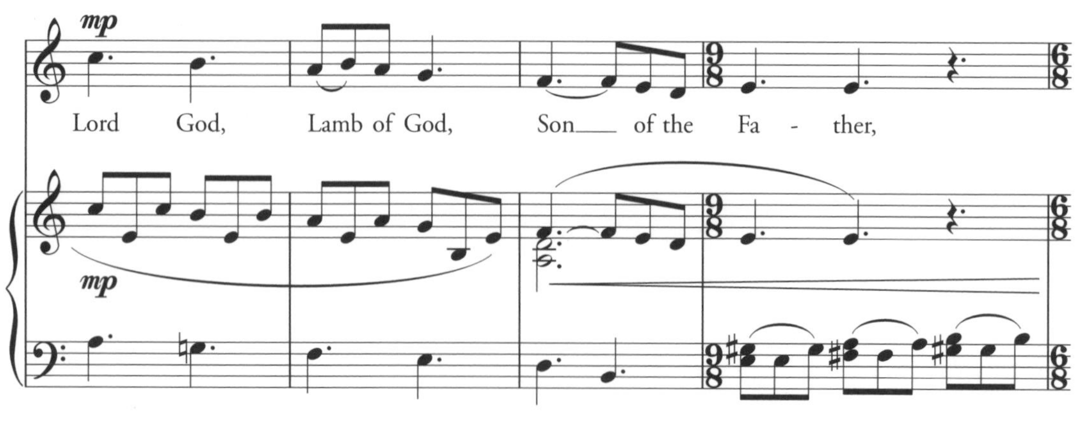
mp
Lord God, Lamb of God, Son of the Fa - ther,
mp

mf
you take a-way the sins of the world, have mer-cy on us;
mf

mp
mf
you take a-way the sins of the world, re - ceive our prayer; you are
mp
mf

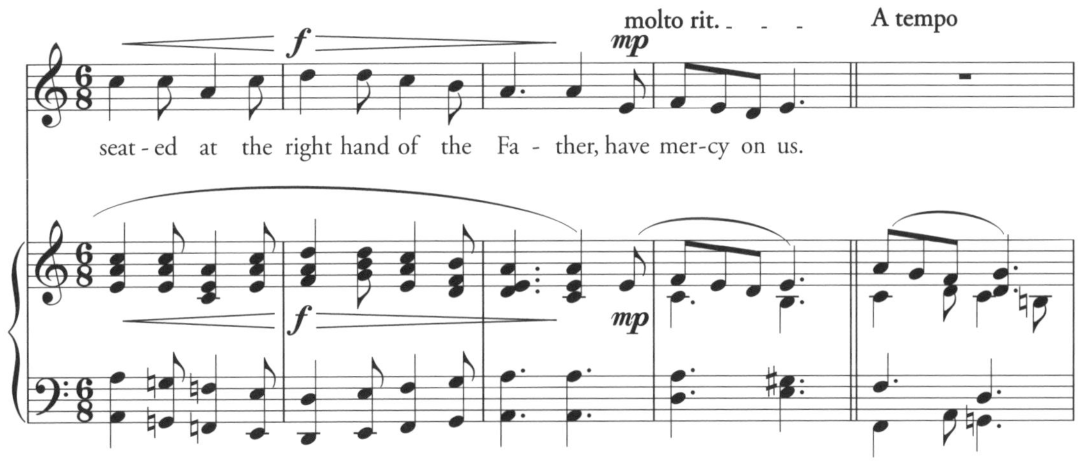
f
molto rit.
mp
A tempo
seat - ed at the right hand of the Fa - ther, have mer-cy on us.
f
mp

mf
For you a - lone are the
mf

Ho-ly One, you a-lone are the Lord,

più f
you a-lone are the Most High, Je - sus, Je - sus Christ,
più f

f
with the Ho - ly Spi - rit, in the glo - ry of God the
f

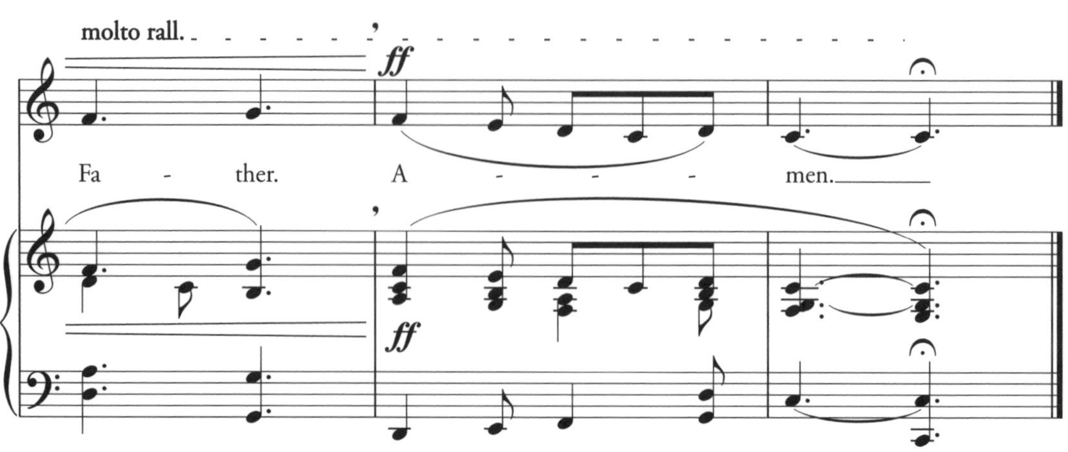
molto rall.
ff
Fa - ther. A - - - men.
ff

Mass of St Kenelm

Holy, Holy, Holy

Alan Smith

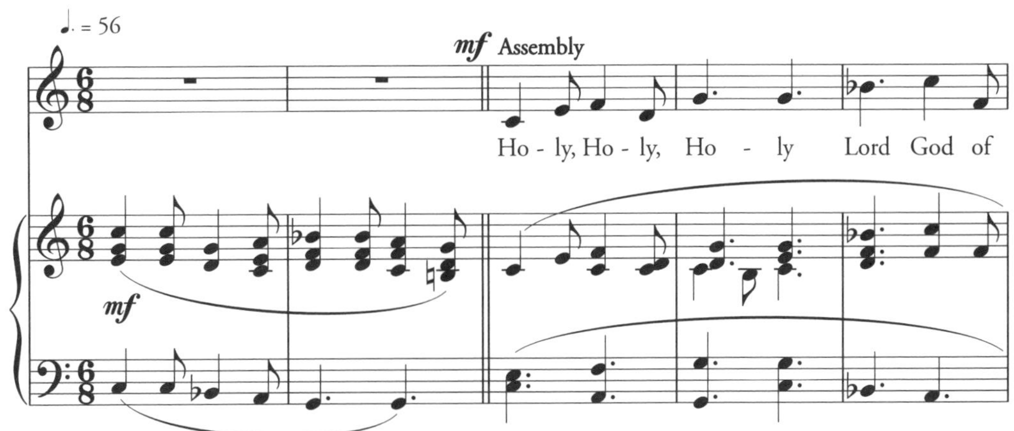
♩. = 56
mf Assembly
Ho - ly, Ho - ly, Ho - ly Lord God of
mf

hosts. Heav-en and earth are full of your glo - ry. Ho-

san - na in the high - est. Bless-ed is he who

comes in the name of the Lord. Ho - san - na in the
molto rit.
high - est.

Mass of St Kenelm

We proclaim your Death

Alan Smith

Strong ♩. = 56
Priest
f Assembly
The mys-tery of faith.* We pro - claim your Death, O Lord,
* or sing the Missal chant, beginning E-G
mp colla voce
f
(piano: add lower octaves)

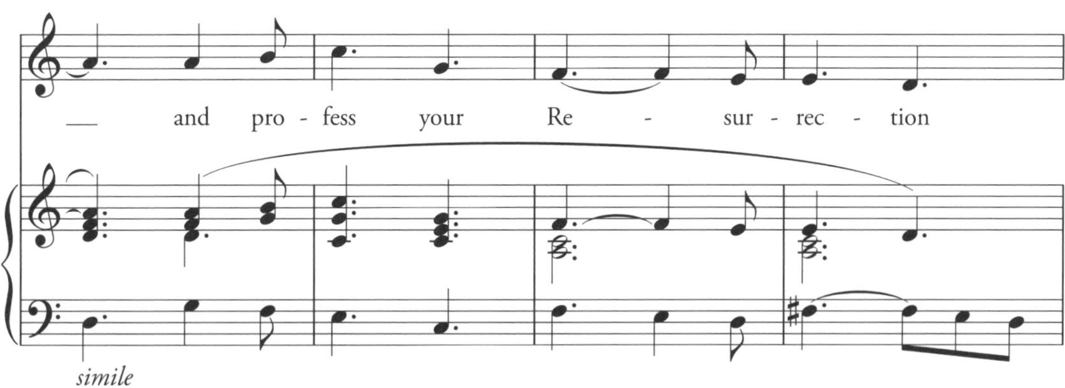
and pro - fess your Re - sur - rec - tion
simile

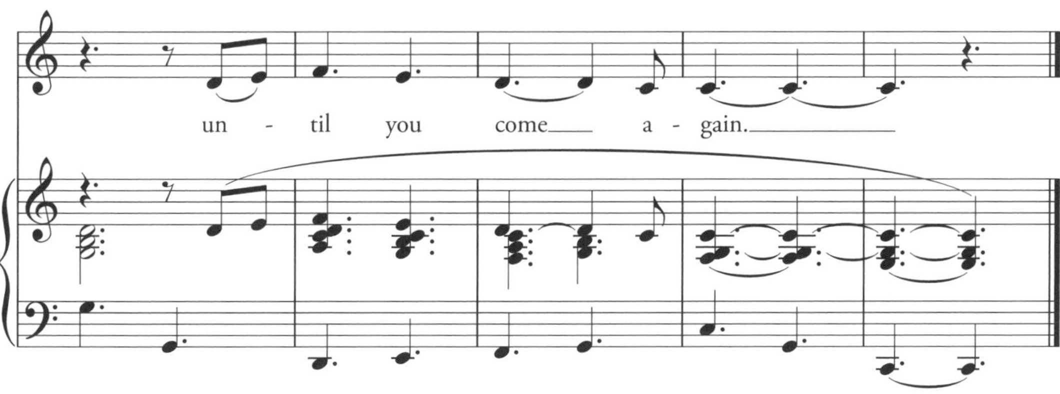
un - til you come a - gain.

Mass of St Kenelm

When we eat this Bread

Alan Smith

Strong ♩. = 56
Priest
f Assembly
The mys-tery of faith.* When we eat this Bread and drink this
* or sing the Missal chant, beginning E-G
mp colla voce
f
(piano: add lower octaves)

Cup, we pro - claim your Death, O Lord,
simile

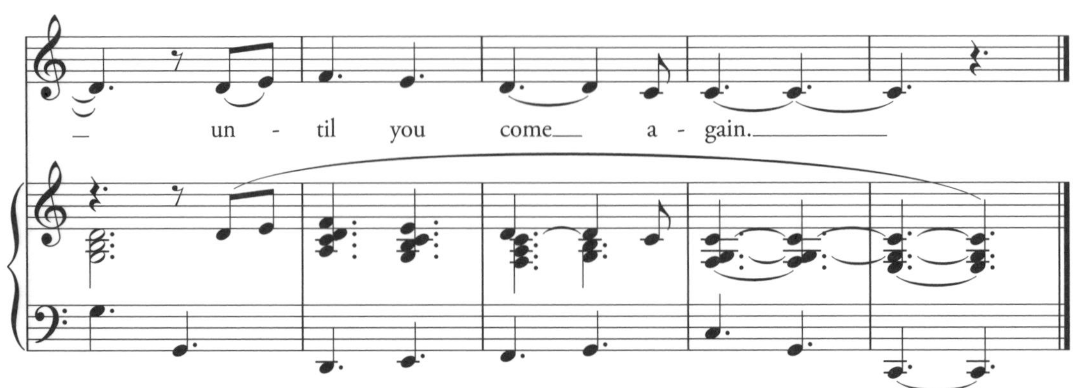
un - til you come a - gain.

Mass of St Kenelm

Save us, Saviour of the world

Alan Smith

Strong ♩. = 56
Priest
f Assembly
The mys-tery of faith.*
Save us, Sa-viour of the world,
* or sing the Missal chant, beginning E-G
mp *colla voce*
f
(piano: add lower octaves)

for by your Cross and Re - sur - rec - tion
simile

you have set us free.

Mass of St Kenelm

Amen

Alan Smith

(spoken)
Strong ♩. = 56
f Assembly
... ev - er and ev - er.*
A men, a -
* or sing the Missal chant, beginning D-F
mp
f
(piano: add lower octaves)
- men,
a - men,
a - men.

Mass of St Kenelm

Lamb of God

Alan Smith

♩. = 35
p All
Lamb of God, you take a-way the
p
sins of the world, have mer-cy on us.
mp
mp
Lamb of God, you take a-way the sins of the world, have mer-cy on us.

mf
Lamb of God, you take a - way the
mf
molto rit.
mp
sins of the world, grant us peace.
mp

Mass of St Luke

Penitential Act

Penitential Act - First form: sing straight through without the pauses.
Penitential Act - Third form: sing each line separately, with the pauses, after the priest's spoken invocations.

Mike Stanley

G C D G
Assembly
mp
Lord, have mer- cy. Lord, have mer- cy. Ky- ri- e, e - lei - son.
Piano
mp
Ped.
simile
G C D G
Christ, have mer- cy. Christ, have mer- cy. Chris - te, e - lei - son.
G C D G
Lord, have mer- cy. Lord, have mer- cy. Ky- ri- e, e - lei - son.

Mass of St Luke

Glory to God

Mike Stanley

♩. = c.76
G D/F♯ D G D/F♯ D G
(Assembly)
Assembly
f Glo - - ri - a
This may be sung all through by everyone, or the people could sing only the refrains.
Piano
f
Am G D/F♯ D C/G G
(Cantor)
in ex - cel - sis De - - o,
mp and on
mp
C D Em D/F♯ G C/G G C/G G
cresc.
earth peace to peo - ple of good will. We praise you, we bless you, we a -
cresc.

MASS OF ST LUKE (Glory to God)

D Em Am D C D Em D/F♯
dore you, we glo - ri - fy you, we give you thanks for your great

G D C/G G C/G G Am
glo - ry, Lord God, heav'n-ly King, O God, al-might - y

D (Assembly) G D/F♯ D G
Fa - ther. f Glo - - ri - a

MASS OF ST LUKE (Glory to God)

Am G D/F♯ D C/G G C D
(Cantor)
in ex - cel - sis De - o.
mf
Lord Jes - us Christ,
mf

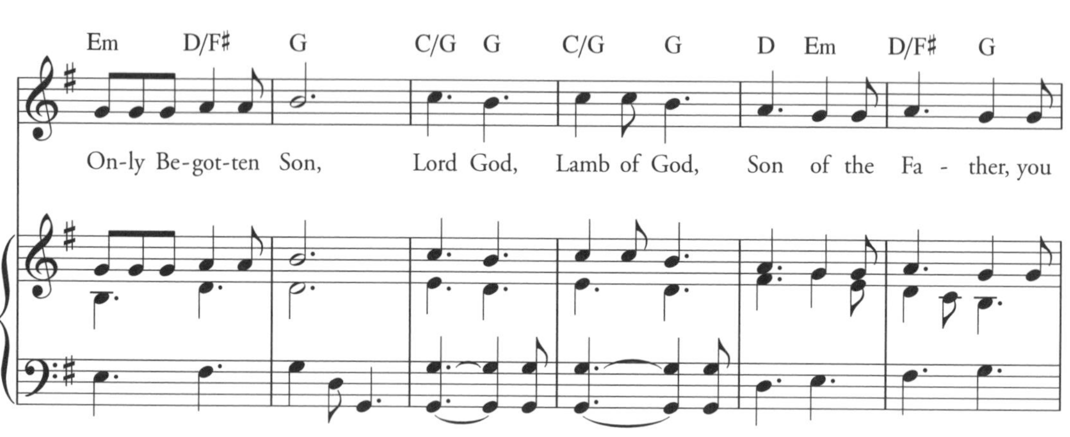
Em D/F♯ G C/G G C/G G D Em D/F♯ G
On-ly Be-got-ten Son, Lord God, Lamb of God, Son of the Fa - ther, you

F C/E D C D Em D/F♯
take a-way the sins of the world, have mer - cy on us, have mer - cy on

MASS OF ST LUKE (Glory to God)

G F C/E D C D Em
us; you take a-way the sins of the world, re-ceive our prayer, re-

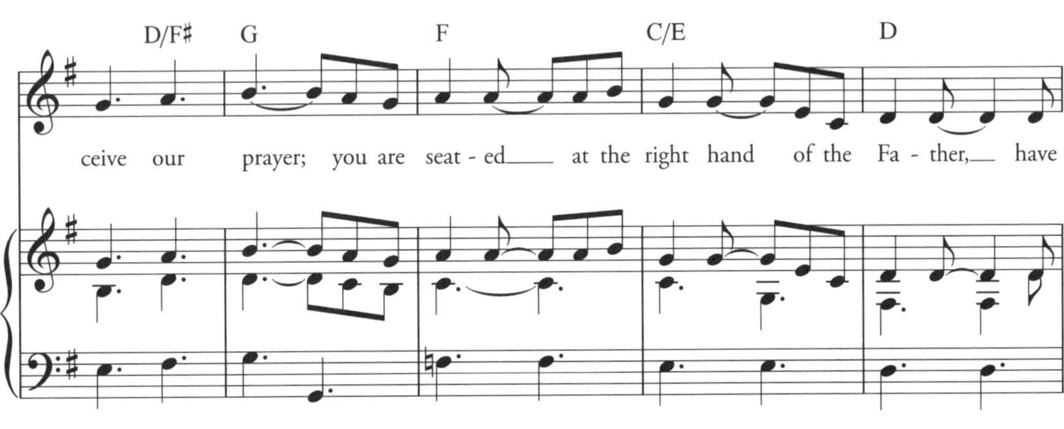

D/F♯ G F C/E D
ceive our prayer; you are seat-ed at the right hand of the Fa-ther, have

C D G Em D/F♯ G D (Assembly) G
mer-cy on us, have mer-cy on us.
f Glo -

MASS OF ST LUKE (Glory to God)

D/F♯ D G Am G D/F♯ D C/G
- ri - a in ex - cel - sis De - o.

G (Cantor) C D Em D/F♯ G C/G G C/G G
For you a-lone are the Ho - ly One, you a-lone are the Lord,

D Em D/F♯ G Am D C D
you a-lone are the Most High, Je - sus Christ, with the Ho - ly

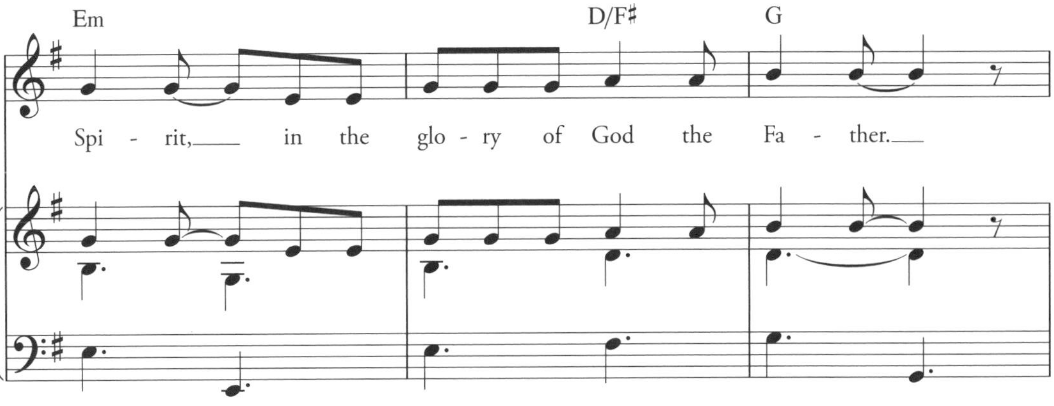

Em D/F♯ G
Spi - rit, in the glo - ry of God the Fa - ther.

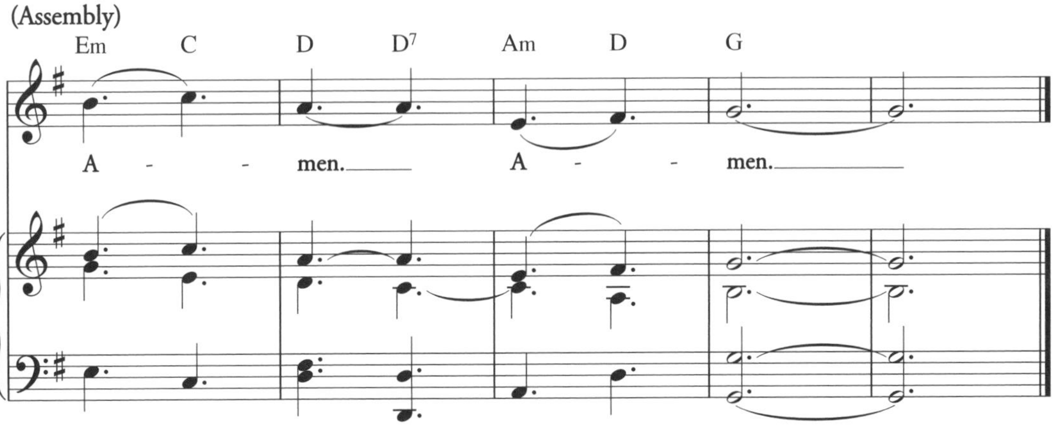

(Assembly)
Em C D D7 Am D G
A - men. A - men.

Mass of St Luke

Gospel Acclamation

Mike Stanley

♩. = c.76
Assembly
Cantor
Piano
mf
Al - le -
Al - le - lu - ia.
G Gm Am7/G G Gm Am7/G G

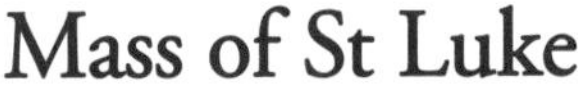

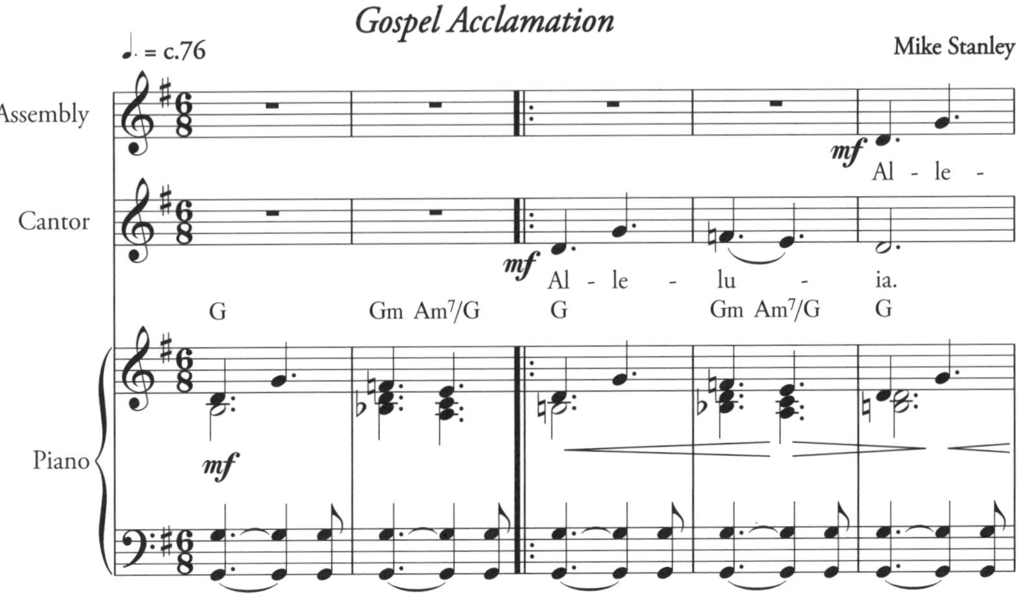

lu - ia. Al - le - lu -
Al - le - lu - ia.
Gm Am7/G G Gm Am7/G G Gm Am7/G
più f

1.
Final
Fine
- ia. - ia.
f Je - sus
Christ, you are the Word of God.
Christ, you are the Word made flesh.
Christ, you are the Prince of Peace.
Christ, you are the Ho - ly One.
G D/F♯ G Em Em7/D C Am7 Dsus4 D
f

Mass of St Luke

Lenten Gospel Acclamation

Mike Stanley

♩. = c.76
Assembly
Cantor
Piano
mf
Glo - ry and
Glo - ry and praise to you, O Christ.
G
Gm Am7/G
G
Gm Am7/G
G

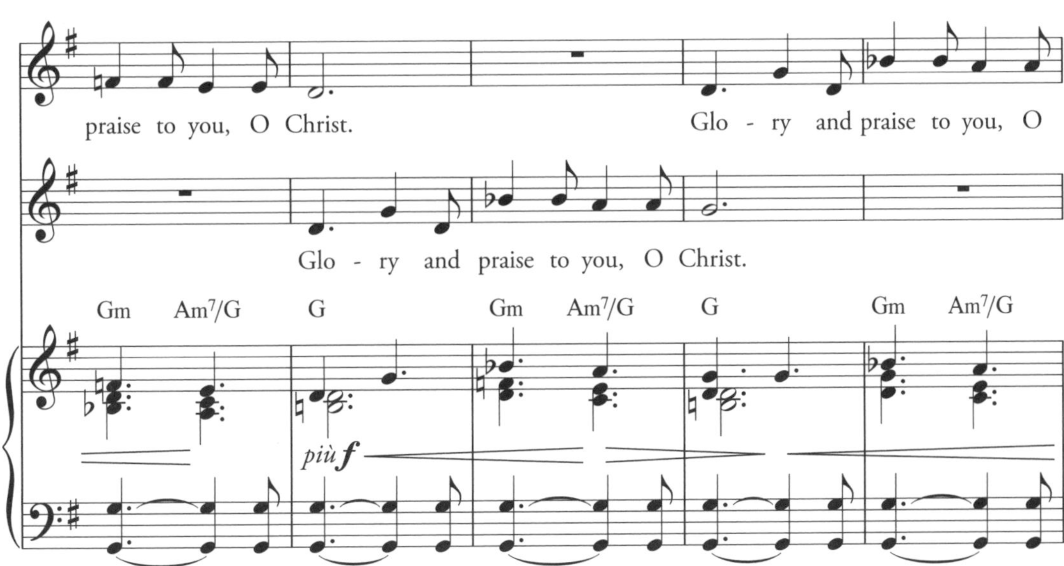
praise to you, O Christ.
Glo - ry and praise to you, O
Glo - ry and praise to you, O Christ.
Gm Am7/G
G
Gm Am7/G
G
Gm Am7/G
più f

1.
Final
Fine
Christ. Christ.
f Je - sus
Christ, you are the Word of God.
Christ, you are the Word made flesh.
Christ, you are the Prince of Peace.
Christ, you are the Ho - ly One.
G D/F♯ G Em Em7/D C Am7 Dsus4 D

Mass of St Luke

Holy, Holy, Holy

Mike Stanley

♩ = c.76

Assembly

Piano

G D D/F♯ Em D C G

mf Ho - ly, Ho - ly, Ho - ly Lord God of hosts. Heav'n and earth are

D G/B C D Em D/F♯ G Am G D/F♯ D

full of your glo-ry.___ Ho - san - na, ho - san - na in the high - est.___ Ho-

MASS OF ST LUKE - Holy, Holy, Holy

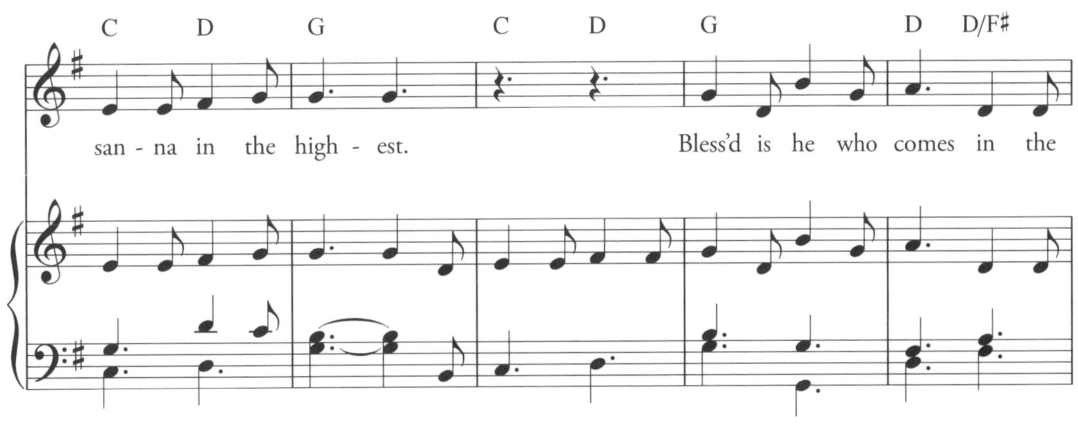
C D G C D G D D/F♯
san - na in the high - est. Bless'd is he who comes in the

Em D C D Em D/F♯ G Am G
name of the Lord. Ho - san - na, ho - san - na in the high -

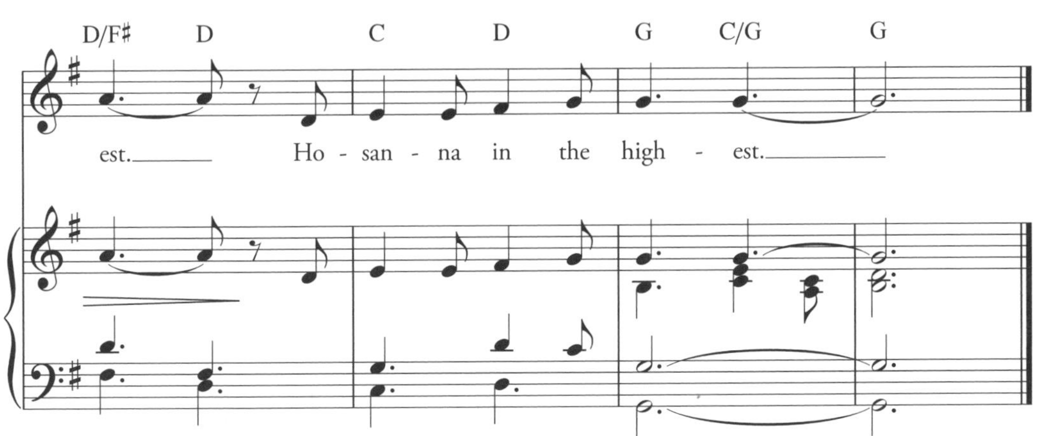
D/F♯ D C D G C/G G
est. Ho - san - na in the high - est.

Mass of St Luke

We proclaim your Death

Mike Stanley

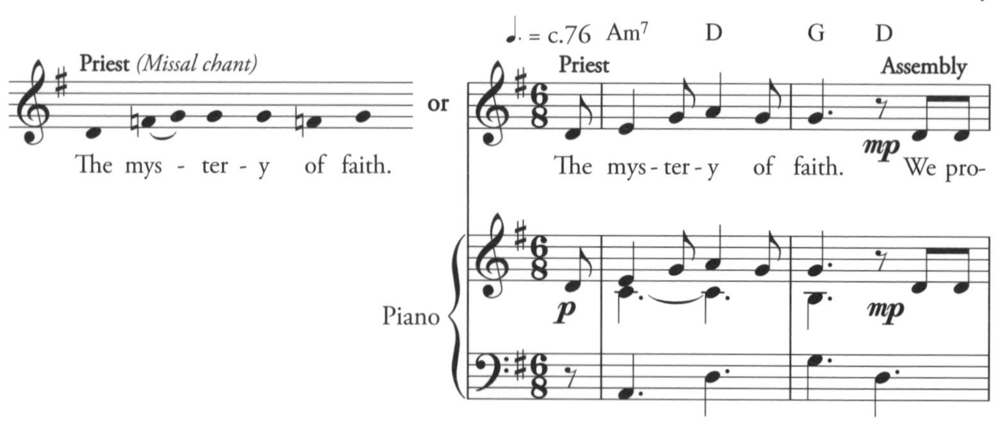
Priest (Missal chant)
The mys - ter - y of faith.
or
♩. = c.76
Am7 D G D
Priest
Assembly
The mys - ter - y of faith. We pro-
mp
Piano
p
mp

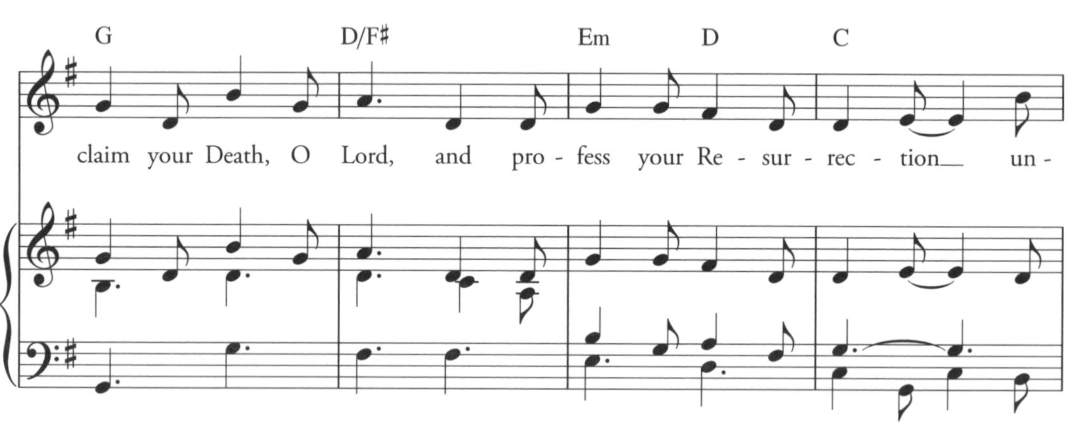
G D/F♯ Em D C
claim your Death, O Lord, and pro - fess your Re - sur - rec - tion un -

Am Em D/F♯ D C D7 E♭ Cm/E♭ G
til you come a - gain, un - til you come a - gain.

Mass of St Luke

When we eat this Bread

Mike Stanley

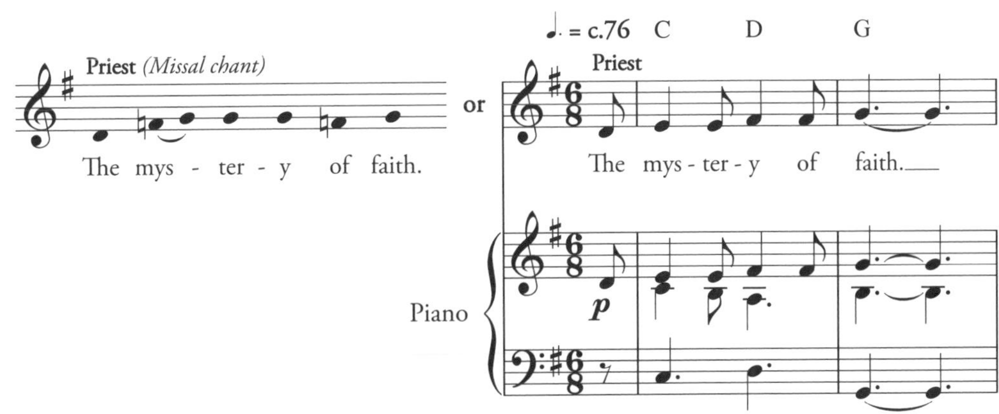
♩. = c.76
C
D
G
Priest (Missal chant)
The mys - ter - y of faith.
or
Priest
The mys - ter - y of faith.
Piano
p

G
D
C
D7
Em
D/F♯
Assembly
mp
When we eat this Bread and drink this Cup,
we pro - claim your Death, O
mp

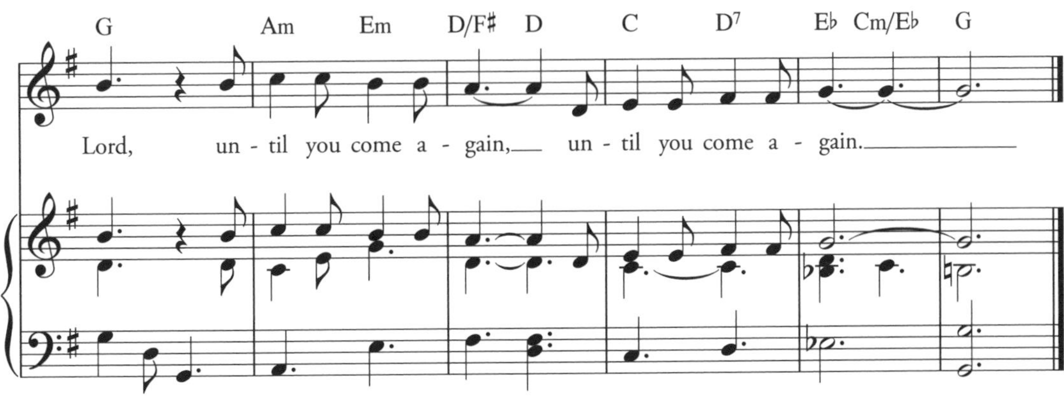
G
Am
Em
D/F♯
D
C
D7
E♭
Cm/E♭
G
Lord, un - til you come a - gain, un - til you come a - gain.

Mass of St Luke

Save us, Saviour of the world

Mike Stanley

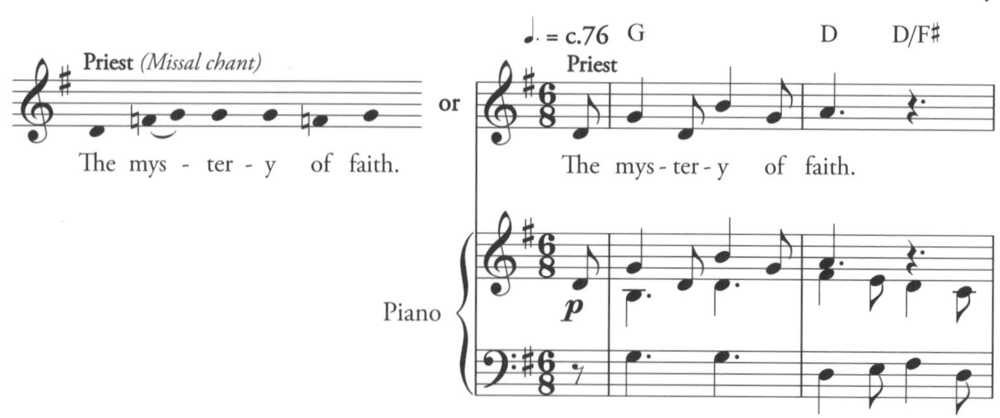
Priest (Missal chant)
The mys - ter - y of faith.
or
♩. = c.76
G D D/F♯
Priest
The mys - ter - y of faith.
Piano
p

G D/F♯ D C D Em D/F♯ G
mp
Save__ us, Sav - iour of the world,__ for by your Cross and Re - sur - rec - tion
mp

Am D/F♯ D C E♭maj7 Cm/E♭ G
you have set us free,____ you have set us free.____

Mass of St Luke

Doxology and Amen

Mike Stanley

♩. = c.69
Em D/F♯ G Am G
Priest
Through him, and with him, and in him, O God, al - might - y
Alternatively, sing this to the Missal chant, beginning E-G, then sing the Amen at ⊕
Piano
mf
D/F♯ D C D B7/D♯ Em Am G
Fa - ther, in the un - i - ty of the Ho - ly Spi - rit, all glo - ry and hon-our is
D/F♯ D C D Em D/F♯ G C D D7 Am D G
Assembly
yours, for ev - er and ev - er. A - men. A - men.
f

Mass of St Luke

Lamb of God

Mike Stanley

♩. = c.63

G D/F♯ D G D/F♯ D C D

Assembly

mp Lamb of God, you take a-way the sins__ of the world,__ have mer - cy on

Piano *mp*

G C/G G D/F♯ D

us.________ *mp* Lamb of God, you take a - way the

mp

G D/F♯ D C D G

rit.

sins___ of the world, *mf* grant us peace.

mf

Pershore Mass

Lord, have mercy

Alan Smith

♩ = 52
Cantor
Assembly
Cantor & Assembly
Lord,_ have mer - cy. Lord,_ have mer - cy. Lord,_ have mer - cy.
Choir (optional)
Lord,_ have mer - cy.
Organ
Lord,_ have mer - cy. Christ, have mer - cy. Christ, have mer- cy. Christ, have
Lord,_ have mer - cy.
Christ, have
[Ped.]

PERSHORE MASS (Lord, have mercy)

Cantor
mer - cy. Christ, have mer - cy. Lord, have mer - cy. Lord, have
mer - cy. Christ, have mer - cy.
p
Assembly
rit.
mer - cy. Lord, have mer - cy. Lord, have mer - cy.
Lord, have mer - cy. Lord, have mer - cy.
mp
Ped.

Pershore Mass

Glory to God

Alan Smith

♩ = 100
Cantor
& Assembly
Choir
(optional)
Organ
mf
Cantor
Glo - ry to God in the high - est, and on earth peace to peo-ple of good will.
Glo - ry to God in the high - est, and on earth peace to peo-ple of good will.
Glo - ry to God in the high - est, and on earth peace to peo-ple of good will.

PERSHORE MASS (Glory to God)

Assembly
f Glo - ry to God in the high - est, and on earth peace to peo-ple of good will.
f
Glo - ry to God in the high - est, and on earth peace to peo-ple of good will.
f
Glo - ry to God in the high - est, and on earth peace to peo-ple of good will.
f

Cantor
f We praise you, we bless you, we a - dore you, we glo - ri - fy you,
f
We praise you, we bless you, we a - dore you, we glo - ri - fy you,
f
We praise you, we bless you, we a - dore you, we glo - ri - fy you,

mf
we give you thanks for your great glo - ry, Lord God, heav'n-ly King, O
mf
we give you thanks for your great glo - ry, Lord God, heav'n-ly King, O
mf

God, al-might-y Fa - ther.
f Assembly
Glo - ry to God in the high - est, and on
God, al-might-y Fa - ther.
f
Glo - ry to God in the high - est, and on
f
Glo - ry to God in the high - est, and on
f

PERSHORE MASS (Glory to God)

f Cantor
earth_ peace to peo-ple of good will. Lord Je - sus Christ,
earth_ peace to peo-ple of good will.
f
earth_ peace to peo-ple of good will. Lord Je - sus Christ,

On - ly Be-got-ten Son, Lord_ God, Lamb of God, Son of the
On - ly Be-got-ten Son, Lord_ God, Lamb of God, Son of the

mf
Assembly
Fa - ther,
you take a-way the sins of the world, have mer - cy, have
you take a-way the sins of the world, have mer - cy, have
Fa - ther,
have mer - cy, have

mp
Cantor
Assembly
mer - cy on us;
you take a-way the sins of the world, re - ceive our pray'r, re-
mer - cy on us;
re - ceive our pray'r, re-
mer - cy on us;
you take a-way the sins of the world, re - ceive our pray'r, re-

PERSHORE MASS (Glory to God)

mf Cantor
Assembly
ceive our pray'r; you are seat-ed at the right hand of the Fa-ther, have mer - cy on
mf
ceive our pray'r; you are seat-ed at the right hand of the Fa-ther, have mer - cy on
mf
ceive our pray'r; you are seat-ed at the right hand of the Fa-ther, have mer - cy on
mf
f (Assembly)
us. Glo-ry to God in the high - est, and on earth peace to
f
us. Glo-ry to God in the high - est, and on earth peace to
f
us. Glo-ry to God in the high - est, and on earth peace to
f

f Cantor
peo-ple of good will. For you a-lone are the Ho-ly One, you a-lone are the
peo-ple of good will.
f
peo-ple of good will. For you a-lone are the Ho-ly One, you a-lone are the

Lord, you a-lone are the Most High, Je-sus
Lord, you a-lone are the Most High, Je-sus

PERSHORE MASS (Glory to God)

mf
Christ, with the Ho - ly Spi - rit, in the glo - ry of God the Fa - ther.
mf
with the Ho - ly Spi - rit, in the glo - ry of God the Fa - ther.
mf
Christ, with the Ho - ly Spi - rit, in the glo - ry of God the Fa - ther.
mf

f (Cantor)
A - men. Glo - ry to God in the high - est, and on earth_ peace to
f
A - men. Glo - ry to God in the high - est, and on earth_ peace to
f
A - men. Glo - ry to God in the high - est, and on earth_ peace to
f

Slighty slower
ff Assembly
peo - ple of good will.
Glo - ry to God in the
A - - men,
ff
(Tenors double Sopranos ad lib)
Slighty slower
ff

rit.
high - est, and on earth peace to peo - ple of good will.
a - men, a - men, a - men.

Pershore Mass

Gospel Acclamation

Alan Smith

♩ = 100
Cantor & Assembly
Cantor
Al - le-lu - ia, al - le - lu - ia, al - le - lu - ia,
Choir (optional)
a2
Al - le-lu - ia, al - le - lu - ia, al - le - lu - ia,
a2
Al - le-lu - ia, al - le - lu - ia, al - le - lu - ia,
Organ
al-le-lu-ia.
Assembly
Al - le - lu - ia, al - le - lu - ia, al - le - lu - ia, al - le-lu-ia.
al-le-lu-ia. Al - le - lu - ia, al - le - lu - ia, al - le - lu - ia, al - le-lu-ia.
al-le-lu-ia. Al - le - lu - ia, al - le - lu - ia, al - le - lu - ia, al - le-lu-ia.

PERSHORE MASS (Gospel Acclamation)

VERSE
Cantor
A tempo
VERSE
mp colla voce
f
Assembly
ff
Al - le - lu - ia, al - le - lu - ia, al - le - lu - ia, al-le-lu-ia.
ff
Al - le - lu - ia, al - le - lu - ia, al - le - lu - ia, al-le-lu-ia.
ff
Al - le - lu - ia, al - le - lu - ia, al - le - lu - ia, al-le-lu-ia.
rit.
ff

Pershore Mass

Holy, Holy, Holy

Alan Smith

♩ = 100
Assembly
Choir
(optional)
Organ
mf
f
Ho - ly, Ho - ly, Ho - ly Lord God of hosts, Lord God of hosts.
Ho - ly, Ho - ly, Ho - ly Lord God of hosts, Lord God of hosts.
Ho - ly, Ho - ly, Ho - ly Lord God of hosts, Lord God of hosts.

PERSHORE MASS (Holy, Holy, Holy)

f
Heav-en and earth are full of your glo - ry. Ho-san-na in the high - est.
mf
rit.
mf
Bless'd is he who comes in the name of the Lord. Ho - san-na in the high- est.
Bless'd is he who comes in the name of the Lord. Ho - san-na in the high- est.

Pershore Mass

We proclaim your Death

Alan Smith

Priest sing either this (Missal chant)
or this
Priest & Assembly
The mys - ter-y of faith.
The mys - ter-y of faith.
Choir (optional)
Organ
♩ = 100
p
mf
Assembly
We pro - claim your Death, O Lord, and pro -
cresc.
We pro - claim your Death, O Lord, and pro -
We pro - claim your Death, O Lord, and pro -

fess your Re - sur - rec - tion un - til you come a - gain.
Re - sur - rec - tion
fess your Re - sur - rec - tion un - til you come a - gain.
fess your Re - sur - rec - tion un - til you come a - gain.
rit.
f

Pershore Mass

When we eat this Bread

Alan Smith

Priest sing either this (Missal chant)
or this
Priest & Assembly
The mys - ter-y of faith.
The mys - ter-y of
Choir (optional)
Organ
♩ = 100
p
faith.
mf Assembly
When we eat this Bread and drink this Cup, we pro-
mf
cresc.
When we eat this Bread and drink this Cup, we pro-
mf
cresc.
When we eat this Bread and drink this Cup, we pro -
mf
cresc.

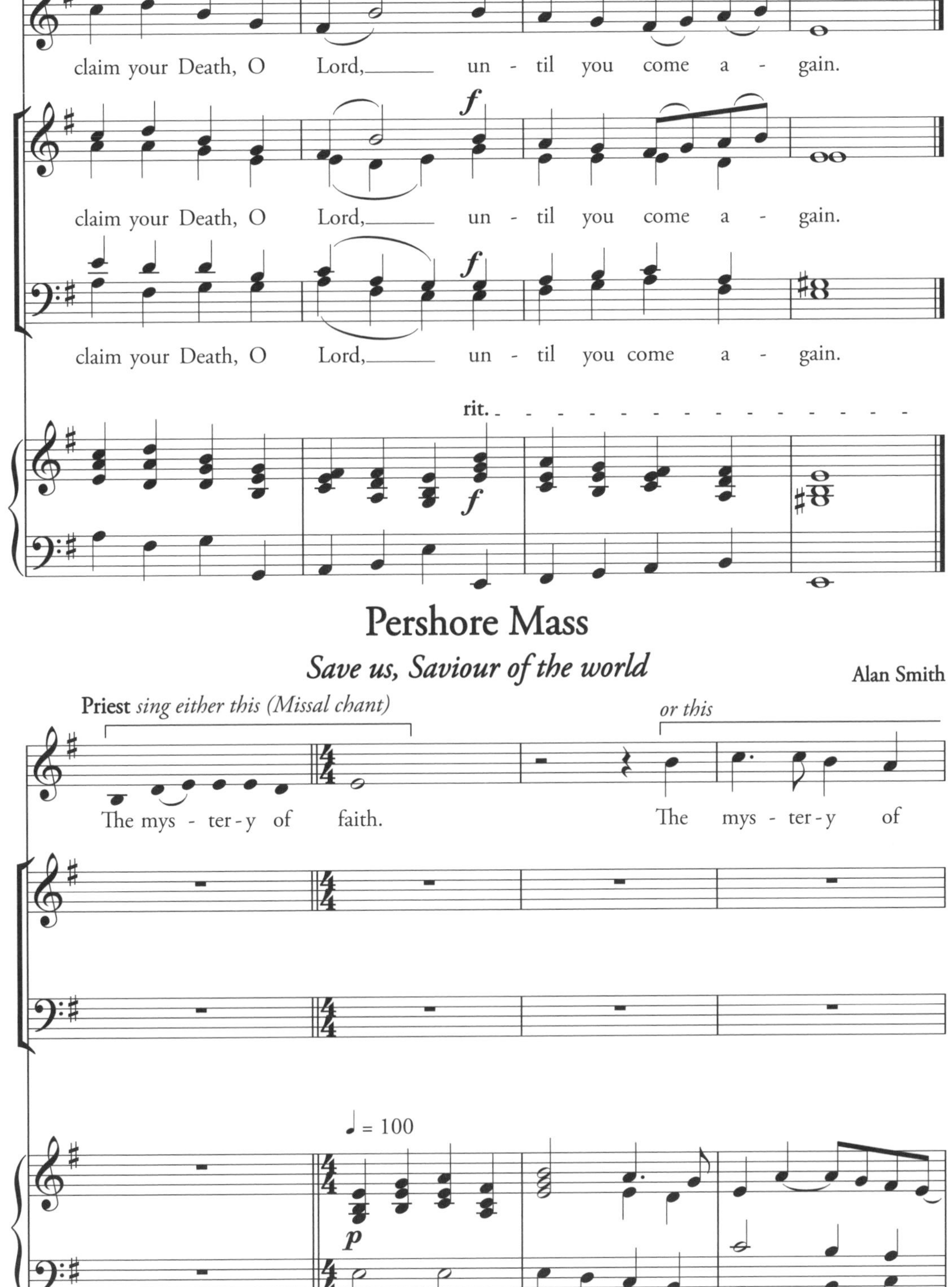
claim your Death, O Lord, un - til you come a - gain.
claim your Death, O Lord, un - til you come a - gain.
claim your Death, O Lord, un - til you come a - gain.
rit.
Pershore Mass
Save us, Saviour of the world
Alan Smith
Priest sing either this (Missal chant)
or this
The mys - ter - y of faith.
The mys - ter - y of
♩ = 100

PERSHORE MASS (Save us, Saviour of the world)

mf Assembly
faith.
Save us, Sa-viour of the world, for by your
mf
cresc.
Save us, Sa-viour of the world, for by your
mf
cresc.
Save us, Sa-viour of the world, for by your
mf
cresc.
rit.
f
Cross and Re - sur - rec - tion, you have set us free.
Re - sur - rec - tion,
f
Cross and Re - sur - rec - tion, you have set us free.
f
Cross and Re - sur - rec - tion, you have set us free.
rit.
f

Pershore Mass

Doxology and Amen

Alan Smith

♩ = 95
Priest
(Alternatively, use the Missal chant (starting E-G) followed by the Amen at *)
Choir
(optional)
Organ
mp
mf
Through him, and with him, and in him, O God, al - might - y
f
Fa - ther, in the u - ni - ty of the Ho - ly Spi - rit, all

glo - ry and ho-nour is yours, for ev - er and ev - er.
*
Assembly
ff A - men, a - men, a - men, a - men, a - men.
A - men,_ a - men, a - men, a - men.
ff
A - men, a - men, a - men, a - men, a - men.
ff (Tenors double Sopranos ad lib)
A - men, a - men, a - men, a - men, a - men.
molto rit.
*
ff

Pershore Mass

Lamb of God

Alan Smith

♩ = 52
Cantor
Assembly
Cantor & Assembly
mp Lamb of God, you take a-way the sins of the world, have mer - cy, have
Choir (optional)
mp
have mer - cy, have
mp
have mer - cy, have
Organ
mp
mf
mer - cy, have mer - cy on us.
Cantor
Lamb of God, you take a-way the sins of the
mer - cy, have mer - cy on us.
mer - cy, have mer - cy on us.
mp

PERSHORE MASS (Lamb of God)

Assembly
Cantor
world, have mer - cy, have mer - cy, have mer - cy on us. Lamb of God, you
have mer - cy, have mer - cy, have mer - cy on us.
have mer - cy, have mer - cy, have mer - cy on us.
mf
mp
[Ped.]
Assembly
take a-way the sins of the world, grant us peace, grant us peace.
grant us peace, grant us peace.
grant us peace, grant us peace.
rit.
mf
Ped.

Sussex Mass

Penitential Act with Invocations

Stephen Dean

♩ = 72
Priest
Cantor or Choir
mf
Ky - ri - e, e - le - i - son.
Organ

Assembly
Priest
Ky - ri - e, e - le - i - son.

Cantor or Choir
Assembly
Priest
Chris-te, e - le - i - son. Chris-te, e - le - i - son.

SUSSEX MASS (Penitential Act with Invocations)

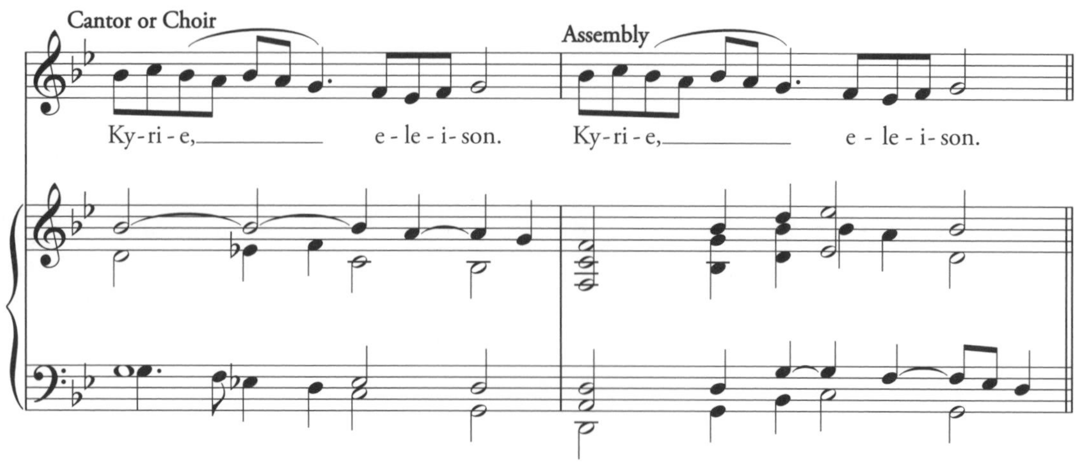
Cantor or Choir
Assembly
Ky-ri-e, e-le-i-son. Ky-ri-e, e-le-i-son.

Priest
May almighty God have mercy on us, forgive us our sins, and

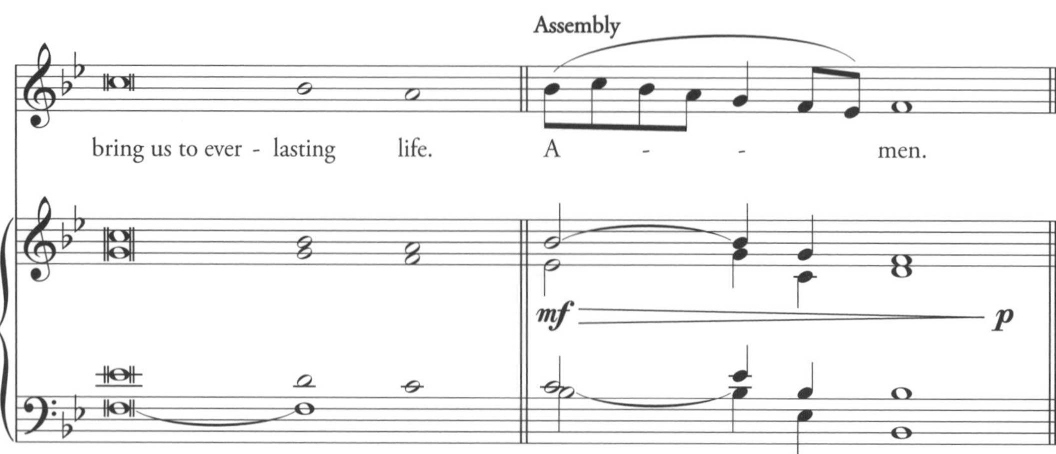
Assembly
bring us to ever-lasting life. A - - men.
mf
p

Sussex Mass

Glory to God (1st setting)

Stephen Dean

♩ = 96
Assembly
Organ
Glo-ry to God in the high-est, and on earth peace to peo-ple of good will. We

praise you, we bless_ you, we a-dore you, we glo-ri-fy you, we give you thanks for your great

glo - ry, Lord_ God, heav-en - ly King, O God, al-might-y Fa - ther.

SUSSEX MASS (Glory to God - 1st setting)

Lord, Je-sus Christ, On-ly Be-got-ten Son, Lord God, Lamb of God, Son of the Fa-ther,

you take a-way the sins of the world, have mer-cy on us; you take a-way the

sins of the world, re-ceive our prayer; you are seat-ed at the right hand of the Fa-ther, have

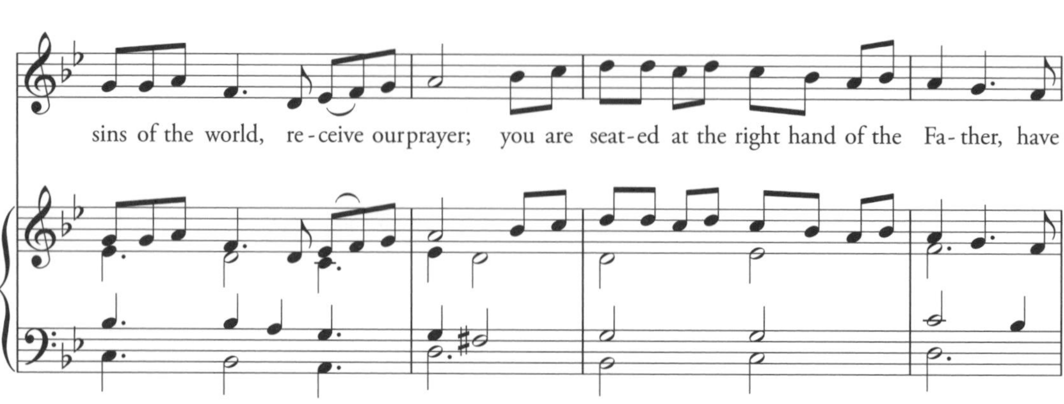

SUSSEX MASS (Glory to God - 1st setting)

mer-cy on us. For you a-lone are the Ho - ly One, you a-lone are the Lord, you a-

lone are the Most High, Je - sus Christ, with the Ho - ly Spi - rit, in the

glo-ry of God the Fa - ther. A - men, a - men.

Sussex Mass

Glory to God (2nd setting)

Stephen Dean

♩. = 70
Assembly
Organ
Glo - ry, glo - ry, glo - ry to God, glo - ry to God in the high -

-est, and on earth, and on earth peace, peace to peo - ple of good

1. (optional repeat)
2.
will. will. We praise you, we bless you, we a -
1. (optional repeat)
2.

SUSSEX MASS (Glory to God - 2nd setting)

dore you, we glo - ri - fy you, we give you thanks for your great glo - ry,
Lord God, heav - en - ly King, O God, al - might - y Fa - ther.
(this refrain is OPTIONAL)
Glo - ry, glo - ry, glo - ry to God, glo - ry to God in the high - est,
(this refrain is OPTIONAL)
and on earth, and on earth peace, peace to peo - ple of good will.

SUSSEX MASS (Glory to God - 2nd setting)

Lord Je - sus Christ, Lord Je - sus Christ, On - ly Be - got - ten Son, Lord God,
Lamb of God, Son of the Fa - ther, you take a -
way the sins of the world, have mer - cy on us; you take a - way the
sins of the world, re - ceive our prayer; you are seat -

SUSSEX MASS (Glory to God - 2nd setting)

ed at the right hand of the Fa - ther, have mer - cy on us. For
you a - lone are the Ho - ly One, you a - lone are the Lord, you a -
lone are the Most High, Je - sus Christ, with the Ho - ly Spi - rit, in the
glo - ry of God the Fa - ther. A - men, a - men.

SUSSEX MASS (Glory to God - 2nd setting)

Glo - ry, glo - ry, glo - ry to God, glo - ry to God in the high - est,

and on earth, and on earth peace, peace to peo - ple of good

will. A - men. A - - men.

Sussex Mass

Holy, Holy, Holy

Stephen Dean

♩ = c.136
Organ
Ho - ly, Ho - ly,

Ho - ly Lord God of hosts. Heav - en and earth are

full of your glo - ry. Ho - san - na in the high - est. Bless-ed is

SUSSEX MASS (Holy, Holy, Holy)

he, bless-ed is he who comes in the name of the Lord. Ho -
-san - na in the high - est, ho - san - na in the high - est.

Sussex Mass

We proclaim your Death

Stephen Dean

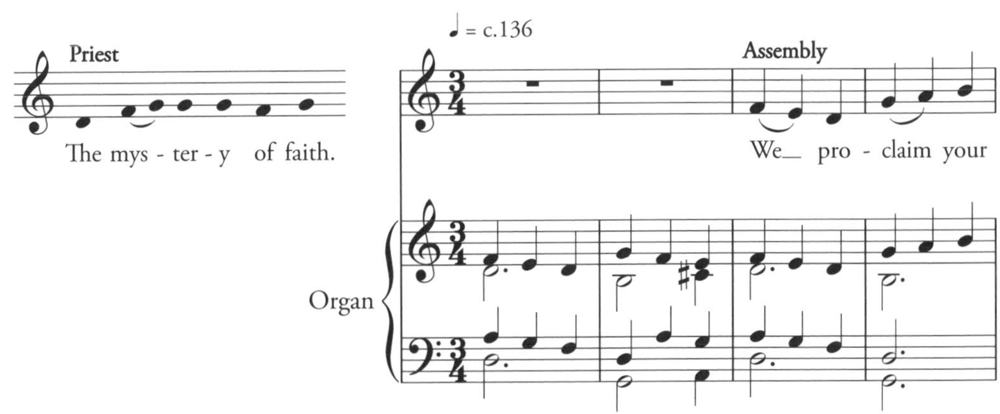
♩ = c.136
Priest
The mys - ter - y of faith.
Assembly
We_ pro - claim your
Organ

Death,_ O Lord, and pro - fess_ your Re - sur - rec - tion un -

til you come_ a - gain,_ un - til you come a - gain.

Sussex Mass

When we eat this Bread

Stephen Dean

♩ = c.136
Priest
The mys - ter - y of faith.
Assembly
When we
Organ
eat this Bread and drink this Cup, we pro - claim your
Death, O Lord, un - til you come a -
gain, un - til you come a - gain.

Sussex Mass

Save us, Saviour of the world

Stephen Dean

Priest
The mys - ter - y of faith.
♩ = c.136
Assembly
Save
Organ

us, Sav - iour of the world,
for by your Cross and Re - sur-

rec - tion you have set us free,
you have set us free.

Sussex Mass

Amen

Stephen Dean

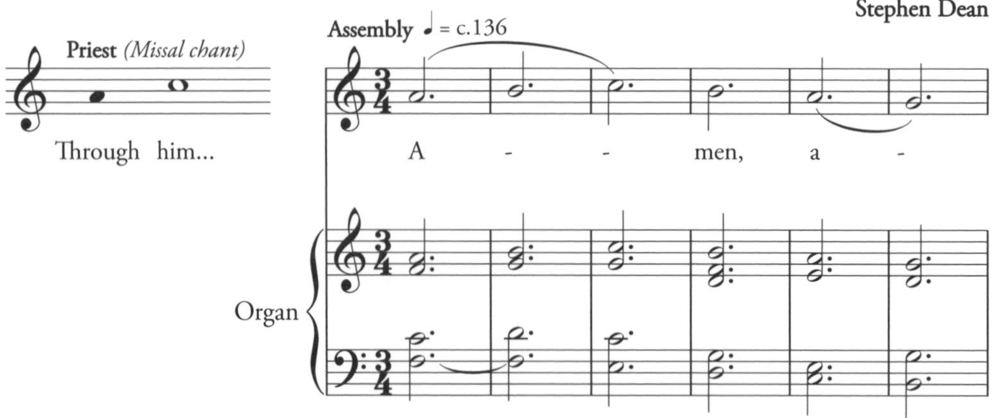
Priest (Missal chant)
Through him...
Assembly ♩ = c.136
A - - men, a -
Organ

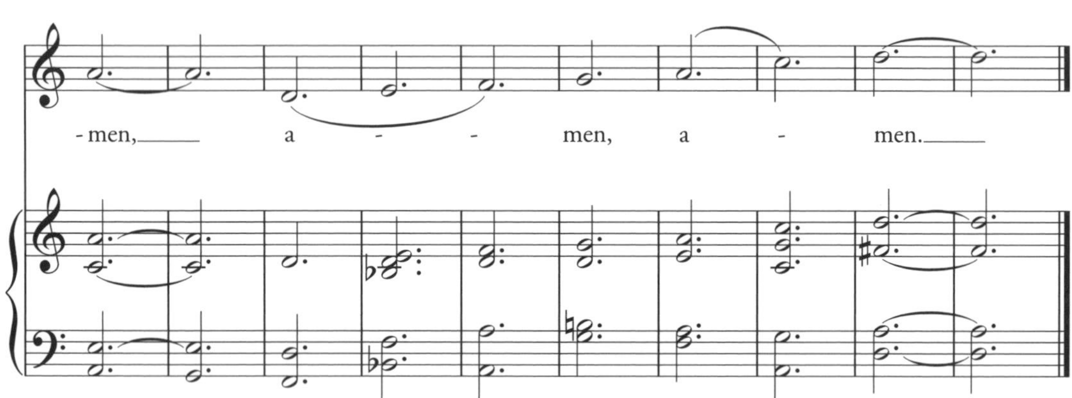
- men, a - - men, a - men.

Sussex Mass

Lamb of God

Stephen Dean

𝅗𝅥 = c.96
Lamb of God, Lamb of God, you take a - way the sins of the

1.2.
world, have mer - cy on us, mer - cy on us,

3.
mer - cy on us.
world,

grant us peace, grant us peace, grant us peace.

The Aston Eucharist

Holy, Holy, Holy

Peter Jones

Joyful ♩ = c96
Capo 7: (Am) (E7) (Am) (E7) (Am) (Am) (E7) (Am) (E7) (Am)
Em B7 Em B7 Em Em B7 Em B7 Em
Assembly
Piano
mf
Ho - ly, Ho - ly, Ho - ly
(Dm7) (G7) (C) (G/B) (E) (Am) (G) (F) (E7)
Am7 D7 G D/F♯ B Em D C B7
Lord God of hosts. Heav'n and earth are full of your glo - ry.
(A) (Dm) (G) (C/E) (Am) (Dm/F) (E7) (Am/E) (E7) (Am)
E Am D G/B Em Am/C B7 Em/B B7 Em
Ho - san - na, ho - san - na, ho - san - na in the high - est.

THE ASTON EUCHARIST (Holy, Holy, Holy)

(Am) (E7) (Am) (E7) (Am) (Am) (E7) (Am) (E7) (Am) (Dm7) (G7)
Em B7 Em B7 Em Em B7 Em B7 Em Am7 D7
Bless'd is he who comes in the name of the
mf
(C) (A) (Dm) (G) (C/E) (Am) (Dm/F) (E7) (Am/E) (E7) (Am)
G E Am D G/B Em Am/C B7 Em/B B7 Em
Lord. Ho - san - na, ho - san - na, ho - san - na in the high - est.

The Aston Eucharist

We proclaim your Death

Peter Jones
Joyful ♩ = c.96
Capo 7: (Am) (E7) (Am) (E7) (Am)
Em B7 Em B7 Em
Priest
The mys - ter - y of faith.
Assembly
mf We pro-
Piano
mf
(Am) (E7) (Am) (E7) (Am) (Dm7) (F/G) (G7) (C) (A)
Em B7 Em B7 Em Am7 C/D D7 G E
claim your Death, O Lord, and pro - fess your Re - sur - rec - tion un -
(Dm) (G) (C/E) (Am) (E7) (Am/E) (E7) (Am)
Am D G/B Em B7 Em/B B7 Em
til you come a - gain, un - til you come a - gain.

The Aston Eucharist

When we eat this Bread

Peter Jones

Joyful ♩ = c.96
Capo 7: (Am) (E7) (Am) (E7) (Am)
Em B7 Em B7 Em
Priest
The mys - ter - y of faith.
Assembly
Piano
mf
(Am) (E7) (Am) (E7) (Am) (Dm7) (G7) (C)
Em B7 Em B7 Em Am7 D7 G
mf When we eat this Bread and drink this Cup, we pro-
(G/B) (E7) (Am) (Dm/F) (E7) (Am/E) (E7) (Am)
D/F♯ B7 Em Am/C B7 Em/B B7 Em
claim your Death, O Lord, un - til you come a - gain.

The Aston Eucharist

Save us, Saviour of the world

Peter Jones

Joyful ♩ = c.96
Capo 7: (Am) (E7)(Am) (Am)
Em B7 Em Em
Priest
The mys - ter - y of faith.
Assembly
mf
Save us,
Piano
mf
(E7) (Am) (Dm) (F/G) (G7) (C) (A)
B7 Em Am C/D D7 G E
save us, Sav - iour of the world, for by your
(Dm) (G) (C/E) (F) (E7) (Am/E) (E7) (Am)
Am D G/B C B7 Em/B B7 Em
Cross and Re - sur - rec - tion you have set us free.

The Aston Eucharist

Amen

Peter Jones

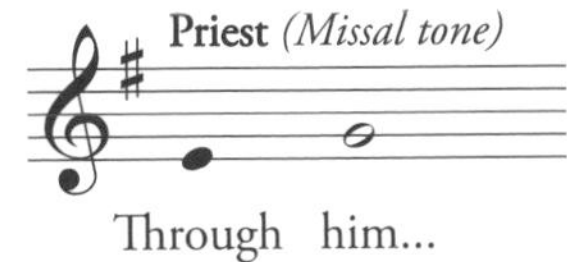

Brandon Acclamations

Holy, Holy, Holy

Stephen Dean

♩ = c.100
Assembly
Organ
f
Ho - ly, Ho - ly, Ho - ly
f
Lord God of hosts. Heav'n and earth are full, heav'n and earth are
mf
crescendo
mf
crescendo
full, heav'n and earth are full of your glo - ry.
f
f

BRANDON ACCLAMATIONS (Holy, Holy, Holy)

Ho - san - na in the high - est,
ho - san - na in the

mf
high - - est.
Bless - ed, bless - ed is
mf

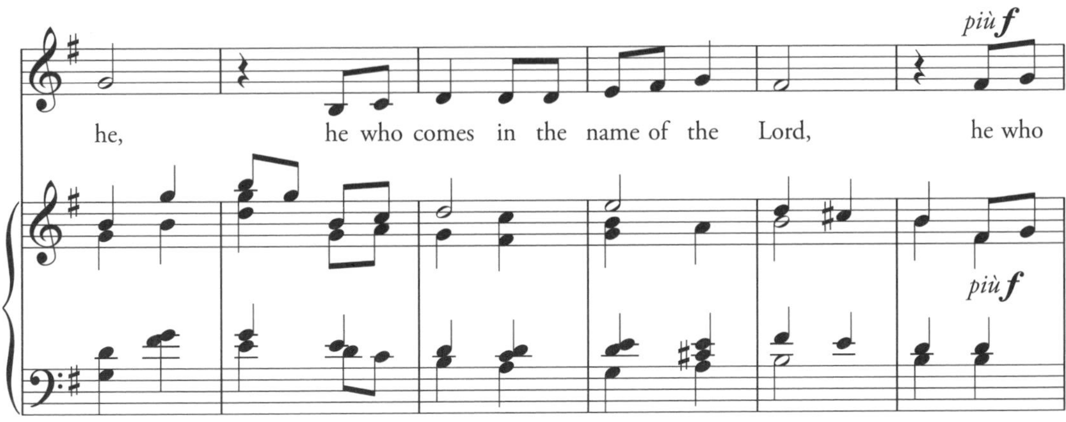
più f
he,
he who comes in the name of the Lord,
he who
più f

f
comes in the name of the Lord.
Ho - san-na in the
f

high - est,
ho - san-na in the high - -

est.
mf

Brandon Acclamations

We proclaim your Death

♩ = c.100
Stephen Dean
Priest
The mys - ter - y of faith.
Assembly
mf
We pro-claim your Death,
Organ
mf
O Lord, and pro-fess your Re - sur - rec - - tion
un - til you come,
un - til you come a - gain.

Brandon Acclamations

When we eat this Bread

Priest
The mys - ter - y of faith.
♩ = c.100
Assembly
Stephen Dean
mf
When we eat this Bread and
Organ
mf
drink this Cup,
we pro-claim your Death,
your Death,
O
Lord,
un - til you come,
un -
til you come
a - gain.

Brandon Acclamations

Save us, Saviour of the world

Stephen Dean

♩ = c.100
Priest
The mys - ter - y of faith.
Assembly
mf
Save us, Sav - iour
Organ
mf
of the world,
for by your Cross and Re - sur - rec - - tion
you have set us free,
you
have set us free.

Brandon Acclamations

Doxology and Amen

Stephen Dean

♩ = c.100
(Missal tone)*
Priest
Through him...
or
*If the Missal chant is sung, begin the accompaniment at ⊕
Organ
mf
Through him, and with him, and in him, O God, almighty Fa - ther, in the
unity of the Ho - ly Spi - rit all glory and honour is yours, for

Assembly
ev - er and ev - er.
A - - men,
a - - - - - - - men.

For the children of the Sacred Heart Primary School, Earlsbury Gardens, Birmingham

Earlsbury Acclamations

This setting of the Eucharistic Acclamations of the Mass is based on a simple ostinato of four chords that are easy to play on a guitar. The lower harmony voice parts and upper descant to the Amen are optional. Non-pitched and pitched percussion ad lib.

Holy, Holy, Holy

Steady
Peter Jones
Leading voices
Ho - ly, Ho - ly, Ho - ly Lord_God of
Assembly
Steady
D B7 Em A D B7 Em A
Piano
hosts.
Heav'n and earth are full of your glo - ry.
Ho - ly, Ho - ly, Ho - ly Lord_ God of hosts.
D B7 Em A D B7 Em A

mf
Ho-san-na in the high-est,
mp
mf
Ho-ly, Ho-ly, Ho-ly Lord_God of hosts.
Bless'd is he who
D B7 Em A D B7 Em A D B7
mf

f
ho - san - na in the high - est,
3 3
comes in the name of the Lord.
Em A D B7 Em A
f

f
ho - san - na in the high - est.
f
Ho - san - na in the high - est.
D B7 Em A Dmaj7
mp

We proclaim your Death, O Lord

Peter Jones

Priest
The mys - ter - y of faith.
Leading voices
mp
We pro-claim your Death, O Lord,
Assembly
mp
We pro-claim your
D B7 Em A D B7 Em A D B7
mp

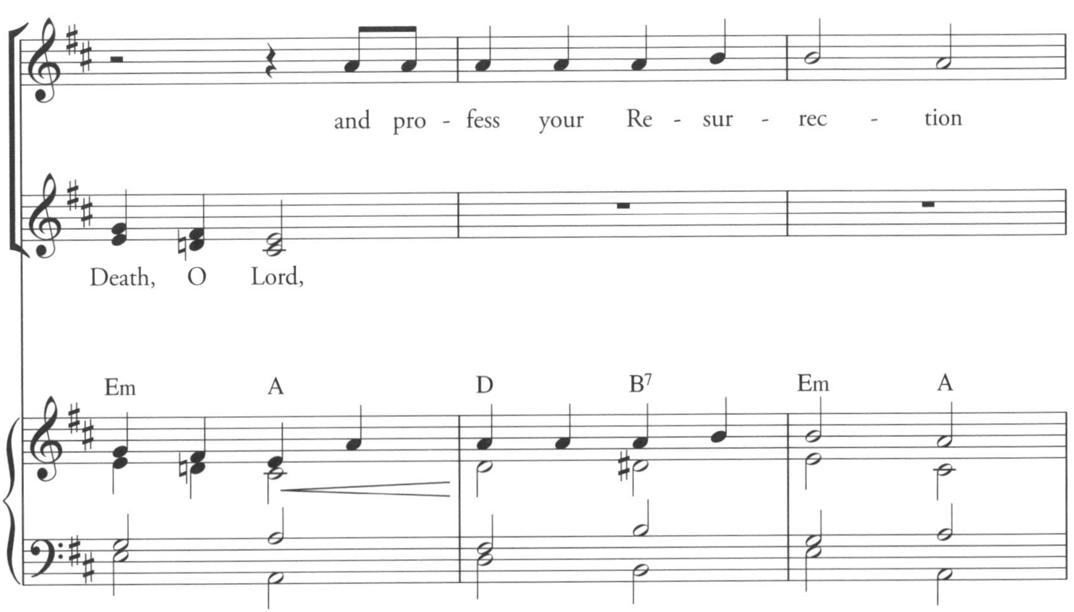
and pro - fess your Re - sur - rec - tion
Death, O Lord,
Em A D B7 Em A

mf
un - til you come a - gain.
mf
un - til you come a - gain.
D B7 Em A Dmaj7
mf

EARLSBURY ACCLAMATIONS

When we eat this Bread

Peter Jones

Priest
The mys - ter - y of faith.

Leading voices

mp

When we eat this Bread and drink__ this

Assembly

D B7 Em A D B7 Em A

mp

Cup,

we pro-claim your

mp

When we eat this Bread and drink__ this Cup,

D B7 Em A D B7

mf
Death, O Lord, un - til you come a - gain.
mf
un - til you come a - gain.
Em A D B7 Em A Dmaj7
mf

Save us, Saviour of the world

Peter Jones

Priest

The mys - ter - y of faith.

Leading voices
mp
Save us, Sav-iour of the world,
Assembly
mp
Save us, Sav-iour
D B7 Em A D B7 Em A D B7
mp

for by your Cross and Re - sur -
of the world, for by your Cross and Re - sur -
Em
A
D
B7

rec - tion you have set us free.
rec - tion you have set us free.
Em
A
D
B7
Em
A
Dmaj7
mp

EARLSBURY ACCLAMATIONS

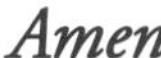

Amen

Peter Jones

Priest (Missal tone)
Through him...

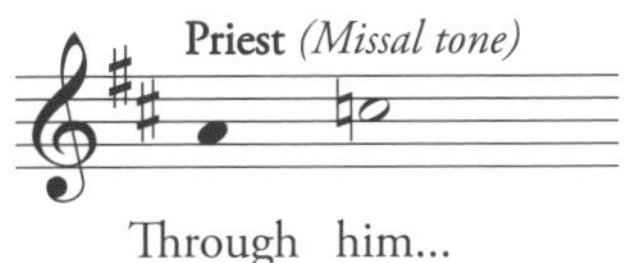

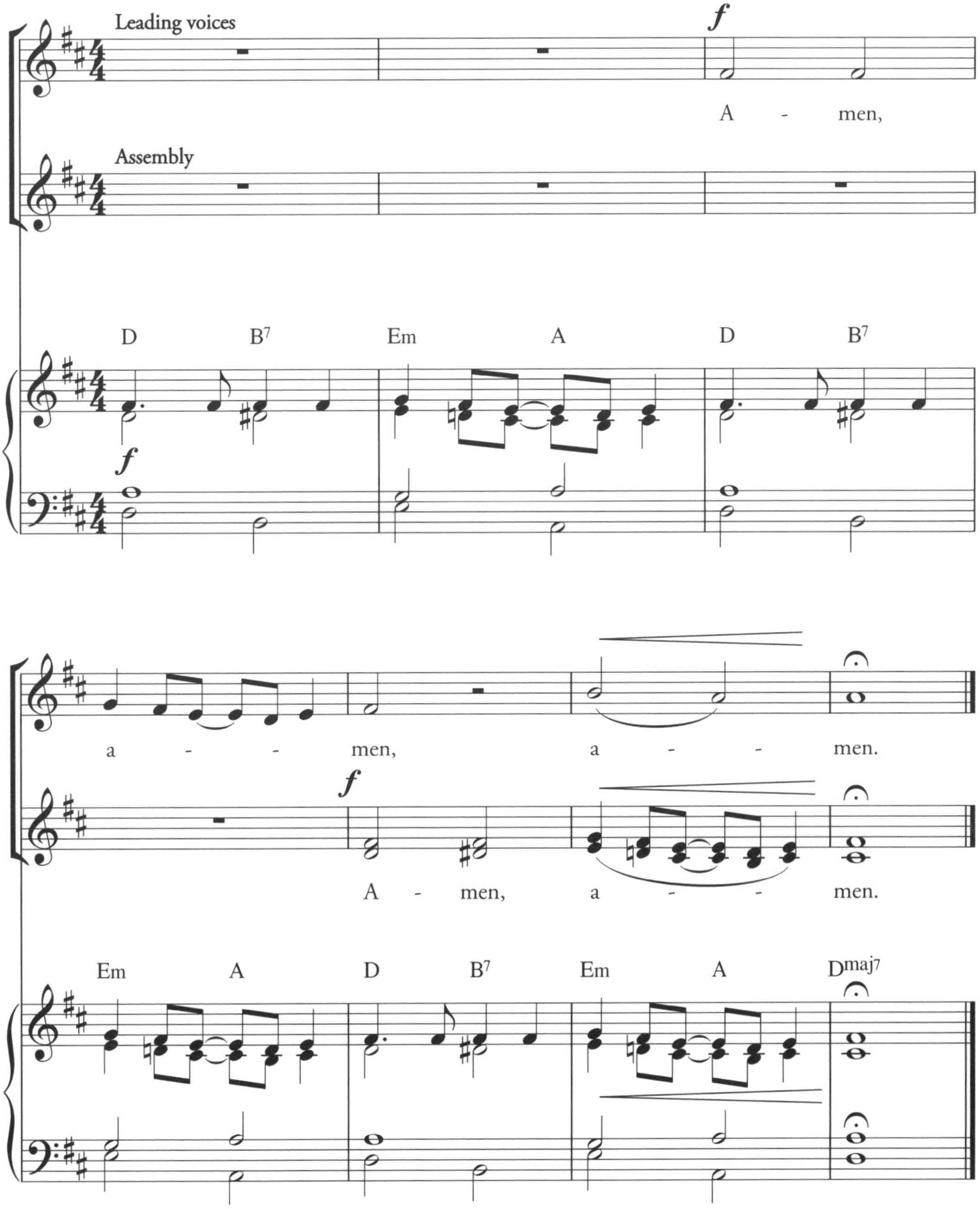

Leading voices
f
A - men,
Assembly
D B7 Em A D B7
f
a - - men, a - - men.
f
A - men, a - - men.
Em A D B7 Em A Dmaj7

In Pace Acclamations

Holy, Holy, Holy

Christopher Walker

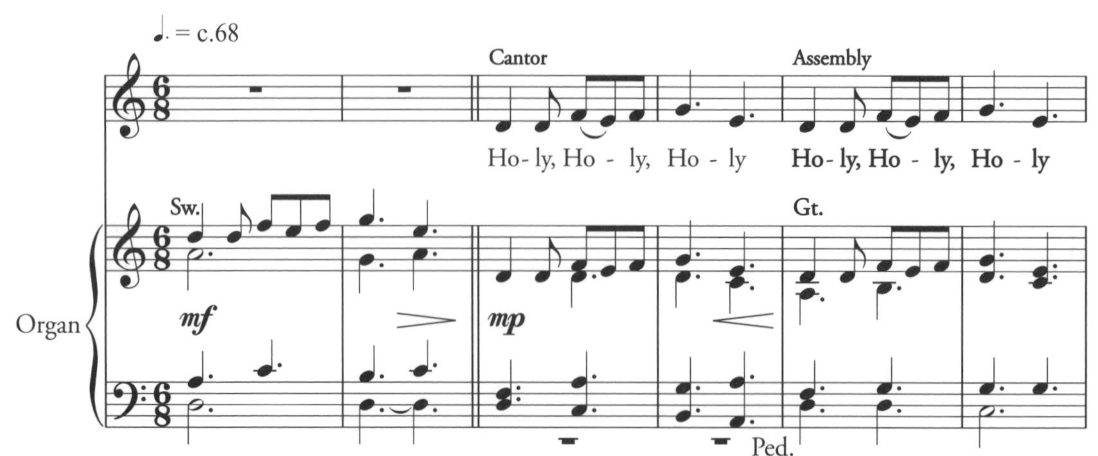
♩. = c.68
Cantor
Assembly
Ho-ly, Ho - ly, Ho - ly
Ho-ly, Ho - ly, Ho - ly
Sw.
Gt.
Organ
mf
mp
Ped.

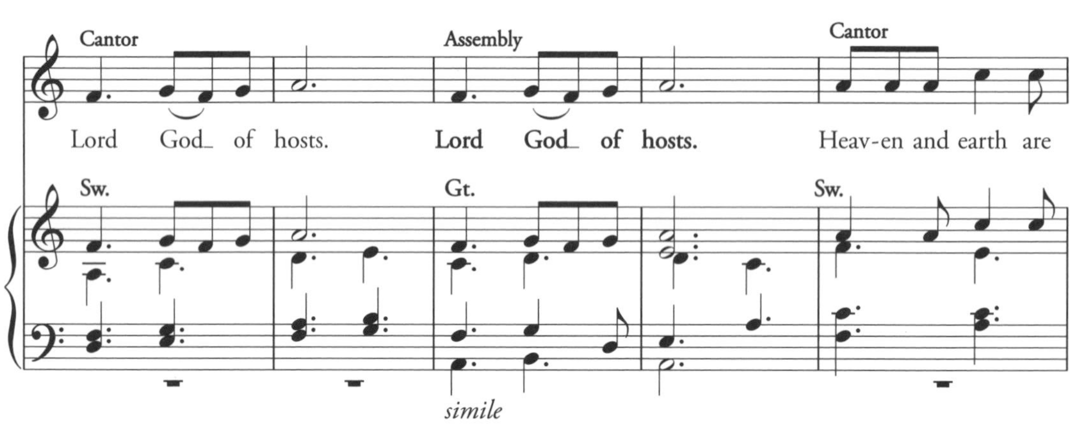
Cantor
Assembly
Cantor
Lord God of hosts.
Lord God of hosts.
Heav-en and earth are
Sw.
Gt.
Sw.
simile

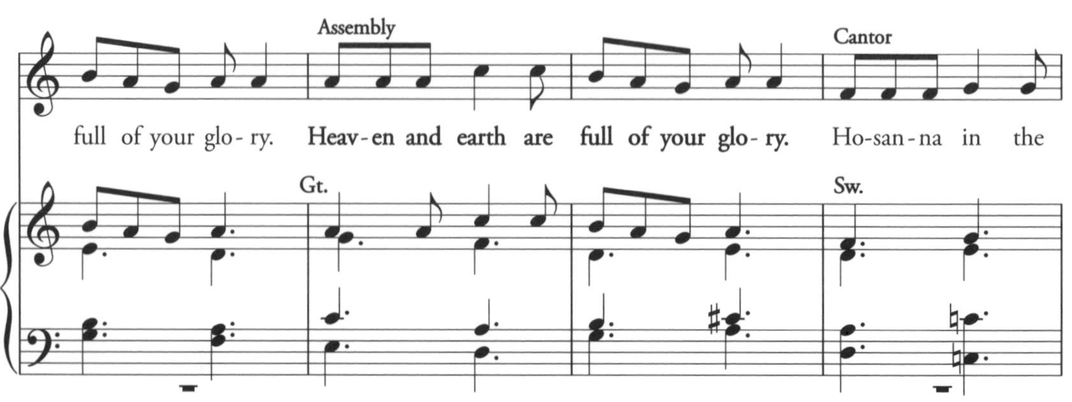
Assembly
Cantor
full of your glo-ry.
Heav-en and earth are full of your glo-ry.
Ho-san-na in the
Gt.
Sw.

Assembly
Cantor
high-est.
Ho-san-na in the high-est.
Bless-ed is he who comes in the name of the
Gt.
Sw.

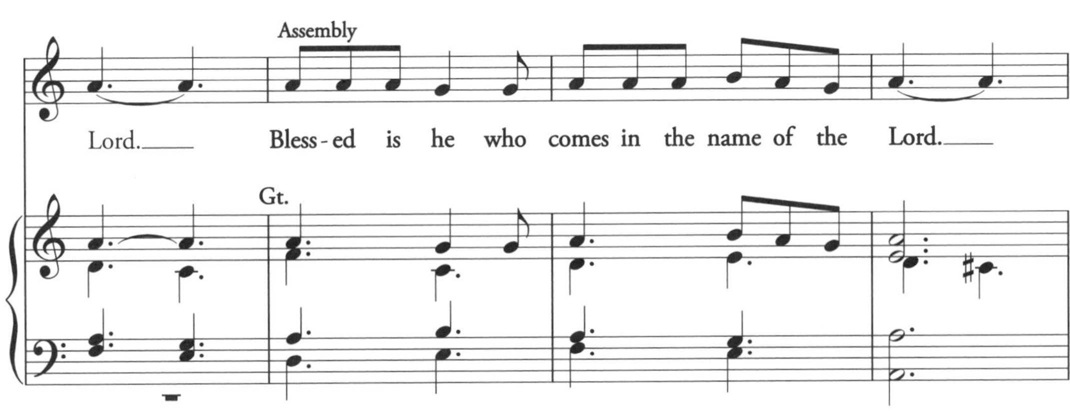
Assembly
Lord.
Bless-ed is he who comes in the name of the Lord.
Gt.

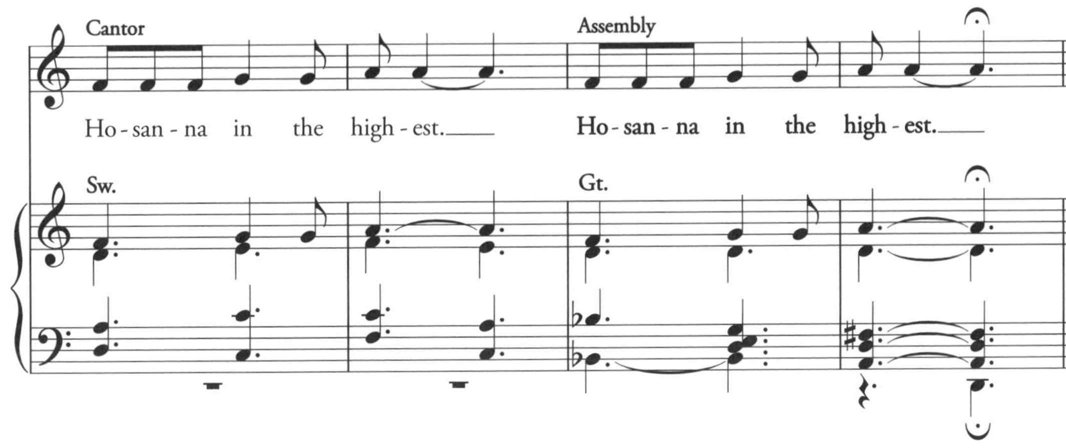
Cantor
Assembly
Ho-san-na in the high-est.
Ho-san-na in the high-est.
Sw.
Gt.

We proclaim your Death

Christopher Walker

♩. = c.68
Priest (Missal chant)
The mys - ter - y of faith.
Sw.
Organ
mp
Cantor
We pro - claim your Death, O Lord,
Assembly
We pro - claim your Death, O Lord,
Gt.
Ped.
Cantor
and pro - fess your Re - sur - rec - tion
Assembly
and pro - fess your Re - sur - rec - tion
Sw.
Gt.
Ped. (simile)

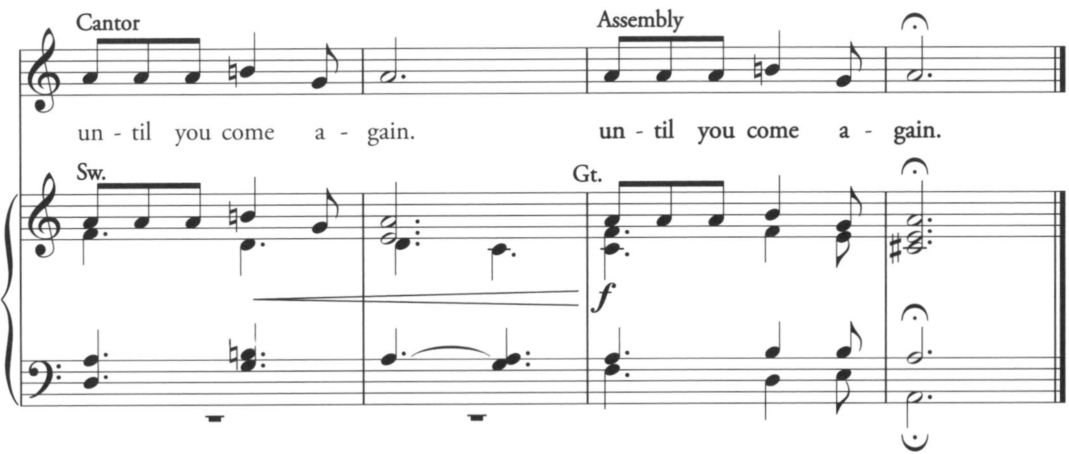
Cantor
Assembly
un - til you come a - gain.
un - til you come a - gain.
Sw.
Gt.

When we eat this Bread

Christopher Walker

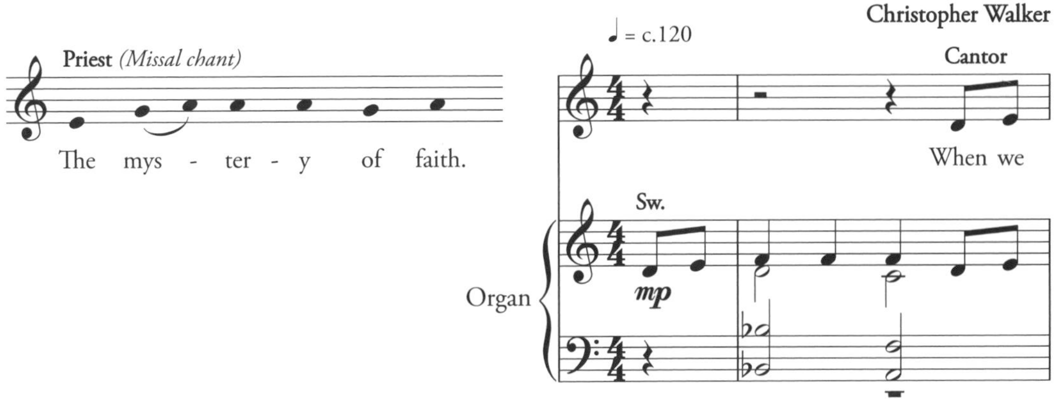
Priest (Missal chant)
The mys - ter - y of faith.
♩ = c.120
Cantor
When we
Sw.
mp
Organ

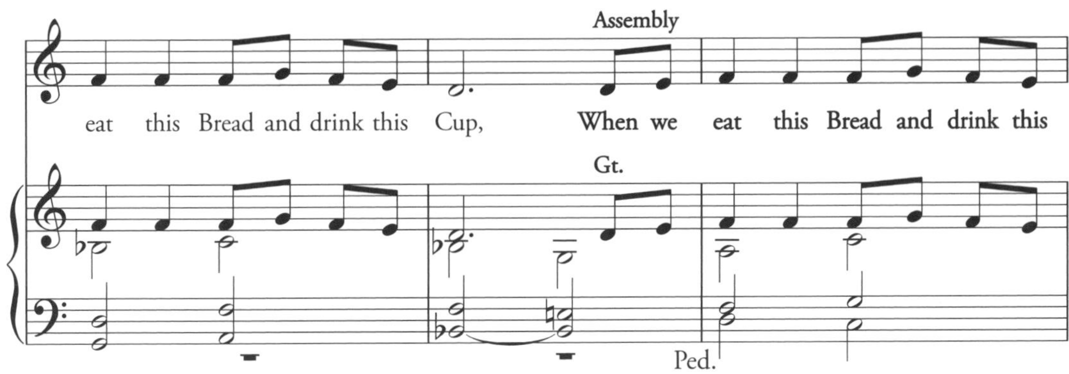
Assembly
eat this Bread and drink this Cup,
When we eat this Bread and drink this
Gt.
Ped.

Cantor
Assembly
Cup, we pro-claim your Death, O Lord, we pro-claim your Death, O
Sw.
Gt.

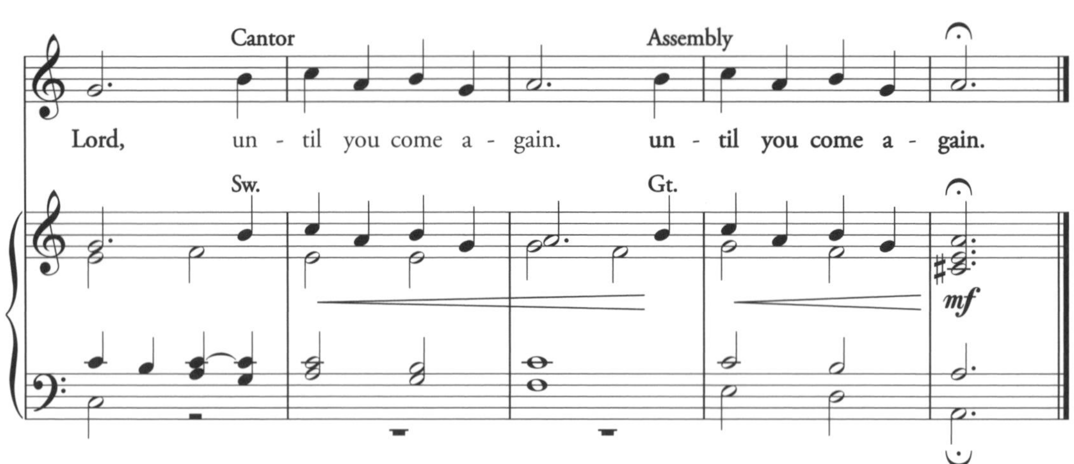
Cantor
Assembly
Lord, un - til you come a - gain. un - til you come a - gain.
Sw.
Gt.
mf

Save us, Saviour of the World

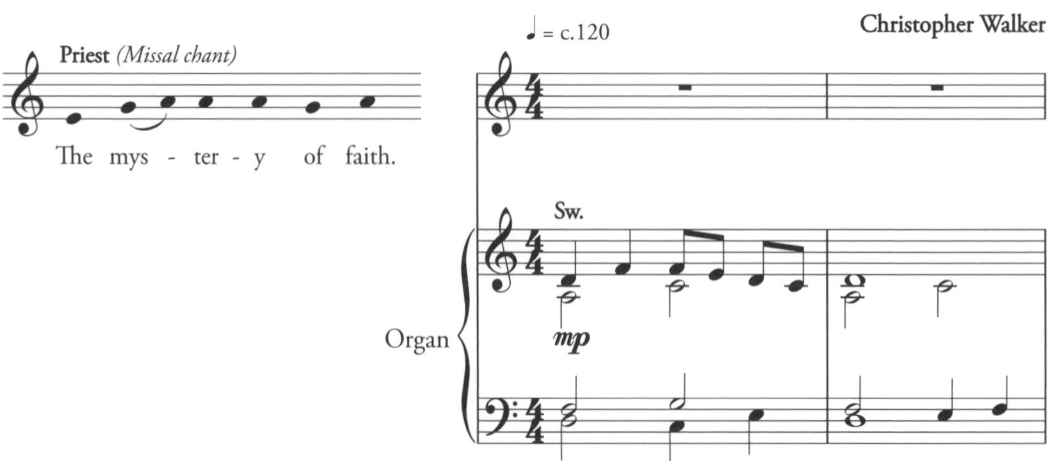
♩ = c.120
Christopher Walker
Priest (Missal chant)
The mys - ter - y of faith.
Sw.
Organ
mp

Cantor
Assembly
Cantor
Save us, Sav-iour of the world,
Save us, Sav-iour of the world,
for by your
Gt.
Sw.

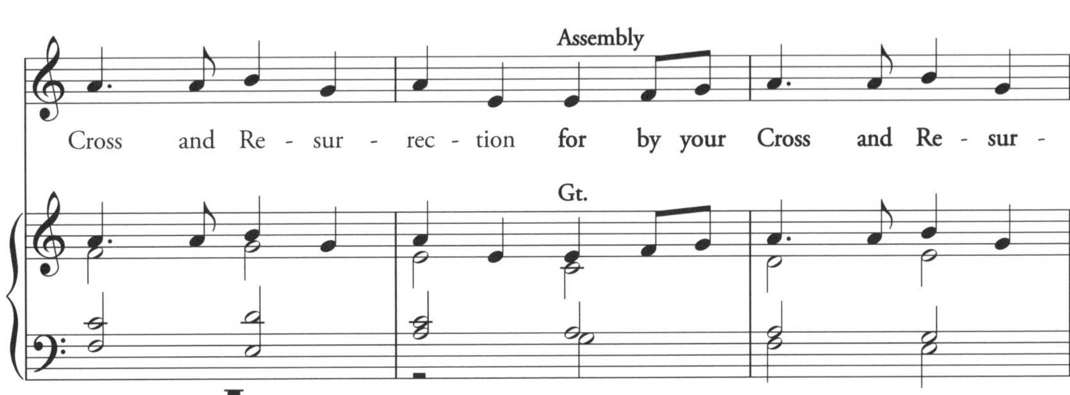
Assembly
Cross and Re - sur - rec - tion
for by your Cross and Re - sur -
Gt.

Cantor
Assembly
rec-tion
you have set us free.
you have set us free.
Sw.
Gt.
mf

In Pace Acclamations

Doxology and Amen

Christopher Walker

Priest (sing in speech rhythm)*
Through him, and with him, and in him, O God, al-might - y
*or sing the Missal chant, beginning E-G
Organ
p

5
(sing in time from here)
Fa - ther, in the u-ni-ty of the Ho - ly Spi-rit, all glo-ry and hon-our is

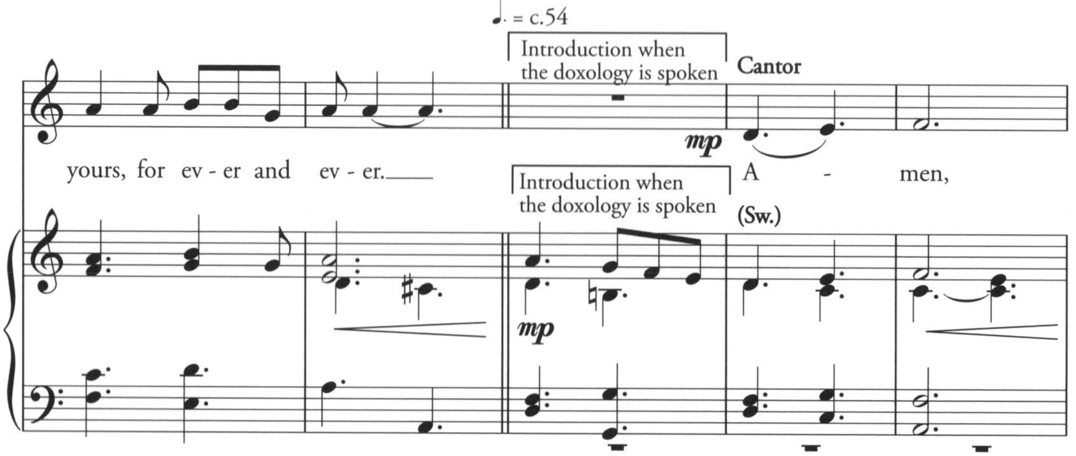
♩. = c.54
Introduction when the doxology is spoken
Cantor
mp
yours, for ev - er and ev - er.
A - men,
Introduction when the doxology is spoken
(Sw.)
mp

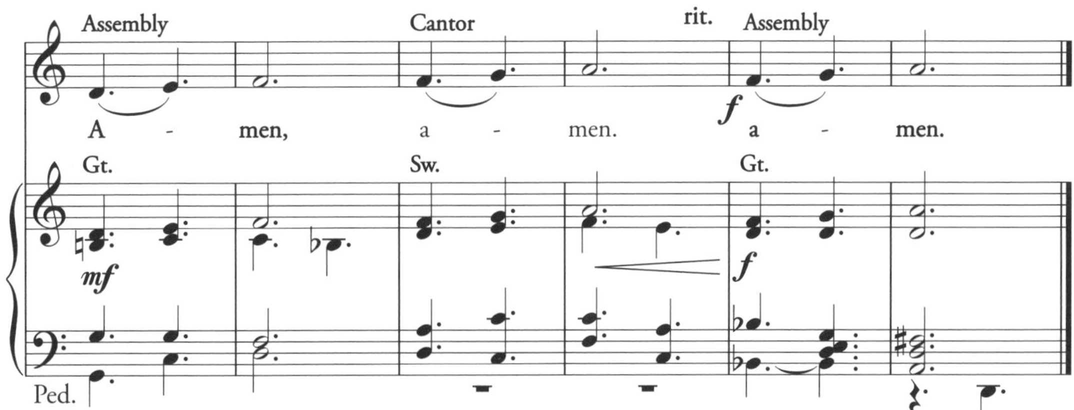
Assembly
Cantor
rit.
Assembly
A - men,
a - men.
f
a - men.
Gt.
Sw.
Gt.
mf
f
Ped.

St Chad's Acclamations

Holy, Holy, Holy

Peter Jones

Moderato 𝅗𝅥 = 52
Choir
(optional)
Cantor &
Assembly
Organ
Cantor
mf
Ho - ly, Ho - ly, Ho - ly
mp
Ho - ly, Ho - ly, Ho - ly Lord God of
Assembly
Lord God of Hosts. Ho - ly, Ho - ly, Ho - ly Lord God of

ST CHAD'S ACCLAMATIONS (Holy, Holy, Holy)

mp
Hosts.
Heav'n and earth are
full of your glo - ry.
mp
Cantor mf
Hosts.
Ho - san -
mp
mf
mf
Ho-san - na.
Ho-san - na.
mf
Assembly
Cantor
Assembly
Cantor
f
- na. Ho-san - na. Ho-san - na. Ho-san - na. Ho - san-na in the high -

f
ff
mp
Ho - san-na in the high - est. Bless-ed is he who
Assembly
-est. Ho - san-na in the high - est.
Lord.
comes in the name, the name of the Lord, the Lord. Ho - san - na, ho-san -
Cantor
Assembly
Ho-san - na. Ho-san -

ST CHAD'S ACCLAMATIONS (Holy, Holy, Holy)

-na,
ho - san - na,
Cantor
Assembly
Cantor
-na. Ho - san - na. Ho - san - na. Ho - san-na in the
ff
ho - san-na in the high - est.
f
ff
Assembly
high - est. Ho - san-na in the high - est.
f
ff

St Chad's Acclamations

We proclaim your Death

Peter Jones

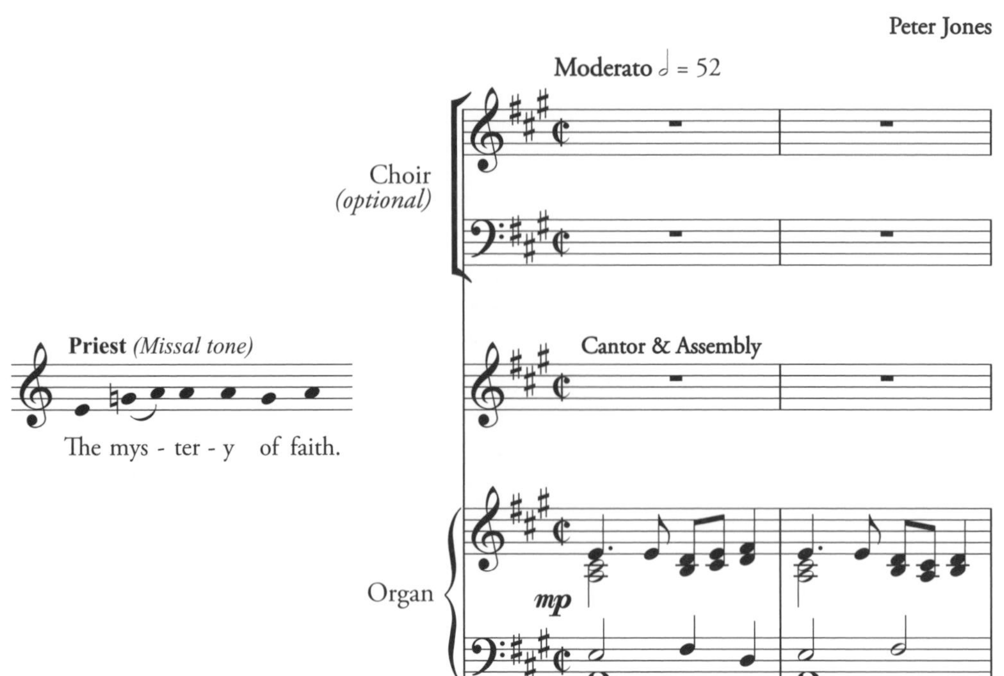
Moderato 𝅗𝅥 = 52
Choir
(optional)
Priest (Missal tone)
The mys - ter - y of faith.
Cantor & Assembly
Organ
mp

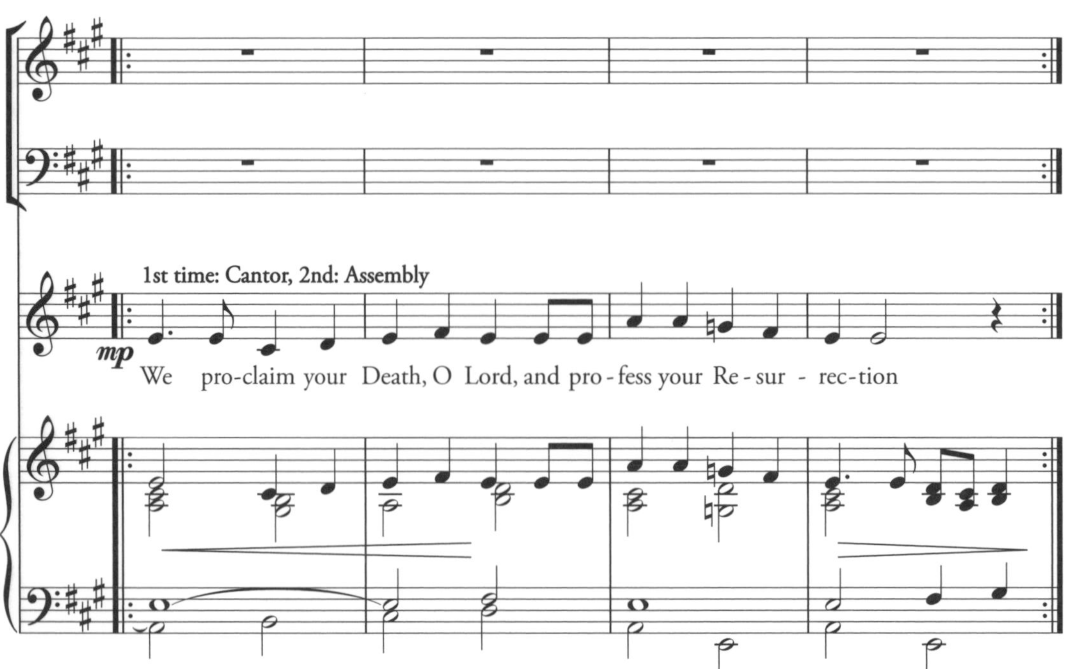
1st time: Cantor, 2nd: Assembly
mp
We pro-claim your Death, O Lord, and pro-fess your Re-sur - rec-tion

mf
un - til you come,
un - til you come,
mf
Cantor
Assembly
Cantor
Assembly
mf
un - til you come, un - til you come, un - til you come, un - til you
f
ff
un - til you come a - gain.
f
ff
Cantor
f Assembly
come, un - til you come a - gain, un - til you come a - gain.
f
ff

St Chad's Acclamations

When we eat this Bread

Peter Jones

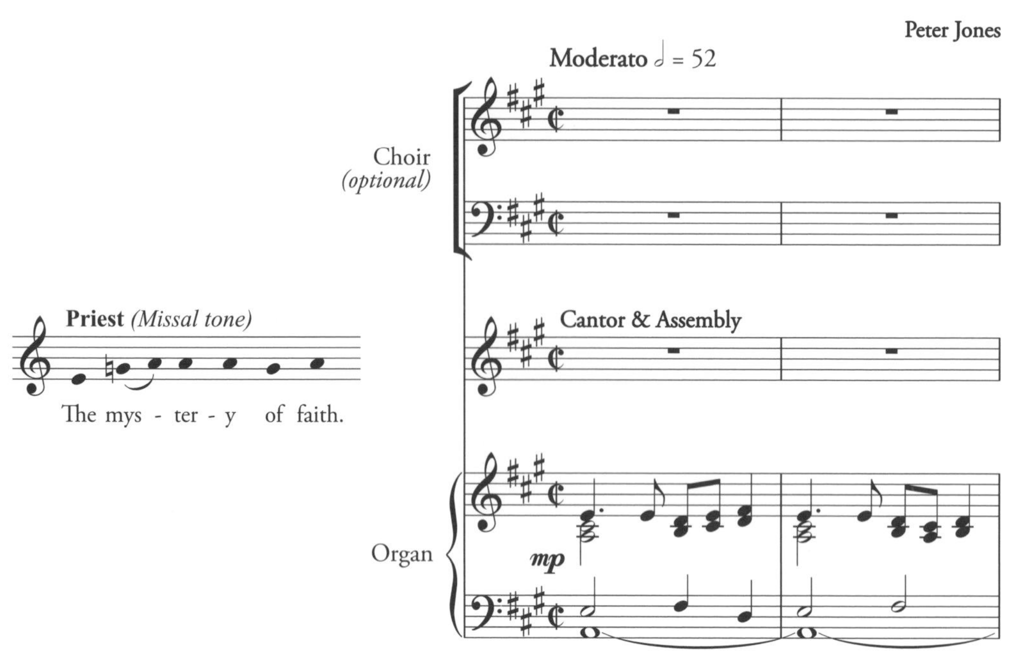
Moderato 𝅗𝅥 = 52
Choir
(optional)
Priest (Missal tone)
The mys - ter - y of faith.
Cantor & Assembly
Organ
mp

mp
When we eat this Bread and drink this Cup, we pro-claim your
mp
Cantor
mp When we eat this Bread and drink this Cup,
Assembly
When we eat this Bread and drink this Cup,

ST CHAD'S ACCLAMATIONS (When we eat this Bread)

mf
Death, O Lord, until you come, until you come,
Cantor
Assembly
Cantor
Assembly
until you come, until you come, until you come, until you

f
ff
until you come again.
Cantor
Assembly
come, until you come again, until you come again.

St Chad's Acclamations

Save us, Saviour of the world

Peter Jones

Moderato 𝅗𝅥 = 52
Choir
(optional)
Priest (Missal tone)
The mys - ter - y of faith.
Cantor & Assembly
Organ
mp
Save us, Sav-iour of the world,
Cantor
Save us, Sav-iour of the world,
Assembly
Save us, Sav-iour of the world,
Cantor
mf
for by your

mf
for by your
mf
Assembly
Cross and Re - sur - rec - tion you have set us free. For by your
mf

f
Cross and Re - sur - rec - tion you have set us free.
Cross and Re - sur - rec - tion you have set us free.
f
Cross and Re - sur - rec - tion you have set us free.
f

St Chad's Acclamations

Doxology and Amen

Peter Jones

Moderato 𝅗𝅥 = 52
Choir
(optional)
Priest (Missal chant)
Through him, and with him, and in___ him...
Cantor & Assembly
Organ
mp
f
Cantor
Assembly
A - men. A - men. A - men. A - men. A -

ST CHAD'S ACCLAMATIONS (Doxology and Amen)

ff
-men.
A - men, a - men.
ff
Cantor
Assembly
-men. A - men, a - men. A - men, a - men.
ff

Spring Sanctus

Holy, Holy, Holy

Martin Barry

Lilting ♩. = 48
Assembly & Choir (optional)
Organ
mf
D Bm G F♯m G Em Asus4 A

Ho - ly, Ho - ly, Ho - ly Lord God of hosts.
mp
Ho - ly, Ho - ly, Ho - ly Lord God of hosts. Heav-en and
Ho - ly, Ho - ly, Ho - ly Lord God of hosts. Heav-en and
mp
Ho - ly, Ho - ly, Ho - ly Lord God, God of hosts.
D Bm Em A F♯m Bm7 Em7 Asus4 A
mp

Heav-en and earth are full of your glo - ry. Ho - san - na in the
earth are full, are full of your glo - ry. Ho - san - na in the
earth are full, are full of your glo - ry. Ho - san - na in the
Heav-en and earth are full of your glo - ry. Ho - san - na in the
D Bm G D Bm7 Em A

high - est, ho - san-na in the high - est.
high - est, ho - san - na in - the high - est.
high - est, ho - san-na in the high - est.
high - est, ho - san - na in the high - est.
F#m7 G D Bm Em A D D Bm

Bless-ed is he, bless-ed is he who comes in the name of the
mp
Bless - ed, bless-ed is he who comes, who comes in the name of the
Bless - ed, bless-ed is he who comes, who comes in the name of the
mp
Bless-ed is he, bless-ed is he, who comes in the name of the
Em Asus4 A D Bm G F♯m7 G Em
mp

f
Lord. Ho - san - na in the high - est, ho - san-na in the
Lord. Ho - san - na in the high - est, ho - san - na in the
Lord. Ho - san - na in the high - est, ho -
san-na in the
Lord. Ho - san - na in the high - est, ho - san - na in the
f
Asus4 A B7sus4 B7 Em A F♯m7 G D Bm Em A

high-est, ho - san-na in the high - - est.
high-est, ho - san-na in the high - - est.
high-est, ho - san - na in the high - - est.
high - est, ho - san - na in the high - - est.
D Bm F♯m Bm Em Asus4 A7 D

Spring Sanctus

We proclaim your Death

Martin Barry

Priest (Missal tone)
The mys - ter - y of faith.
or
Priest
The myster-y of faith.
Organ
Lilting ♩. = 48
Assembly & optional Choir
mp a2
We_ pro-claim your Death, O Lord, and pro-
a2
mp
G Em Asus4 A D Bm Em A
mf
mp
fess your Re - sur - rec - tion_ un - til_ you come a - gain._
F♯m7 Bm7 Em7 Asus4 A D G6 D

Spring Sanctus

When we eat this Bread

Martin Barry

Priest (Missal tone)
The mys - ter - y of faith.
or
Priest
The myster - y of faith.
Organ
Lilting ♩. = 48
Assembly & optional Choir
mp a2
When we eat this Bread and drink this Cup, we pro-
a2
mp
D Bm Em A D Bm Em A
mf
mp
claim your Death, O Lord, un - til you come a - gain.
F♯m7 Bm7 Em7 Asus4 A D G6 D

Spring Sanctus

Save us, Saviour of the world

Martin Barry

Priest (Missal tone)
The mys - ter - y of faith.
or
Priest
The myster - y of faith.
Organ
Lilting ♩. = 48
Assembly & optional Choir
mp
a2
Save us, Sa - viour of the world, for
by your Cross and Re - sur - rec - tion you have set us free.
G Em D D7/F♯ G Em F♯m A/C♯
mf
D Bm G F♯m7 G G6 D
f

Spring Sanctus

Doxology and Amen (1)

Martin Barry

Priest (Missal tone)
Through him, and with him and in him ...
Broader ♩. = 40
... for ev - er and ev - er.
D Bm7 G F♯m7 G G6 D
Assembly
A - men, a - men, a - men.
A - men, a - men, a - men.
f
A - men, a - men, a - men.
A - men, a - men, a - men.
A - men, a - men, a - men.
f

Doxology and Amen (2)

Martin Barry

Priest
D
F♯m7/C♯
Bm
A7
Bm
Through him, and with him, and in him, O God, al - might - y Father, in the
G
Em
Asus4 A
F♯m7
Bm
Em
unity of the Ho - ly___ Spirit, all glory and honour is yours, for ev - er and
Asus4
A
D
Bm7
G
F♯m7
G
G6
D
Assembly
ev-er.___ A - men, a - men, a - men.
A - men, a - - men, a - men.
Optional Choir
f
A - men, a - men, a - - men.
A - men, a - men, a - men.
A - men, a - men, a - - men.
f
Broader ♩. = 40
f

For the Poor Clares of Ty Mam Duw

St Clare Acclamations

Holy, Holy, Holy

Nick Baty

♩ = 110
Em
B7
Assembly
Em
mf
Ho - ly,
Piano
mf

D
G
Am
Ho - ly, Ho - ly Lord, God of hosts.

G
B7
Em
E7
Heav'n and earth are full of your glo - ry.

ST CLARE ACCLAMATIONS (Holy, Holy, Holy)

Am
f
D
G
C
Am
B7
Ho-san - na,
ho-san - na,
ho-san-na in the
f

Em
E7
Am
D
G
C
high - est.
Ho-san - na,
ho-san - na,
3

Am
B7
Em
B7
ho-san-na in the high - est.
mf

ST CLARE ACCLAMATIONS (Holy, Holy, Holy)

Em
C
D
mf Bless-ed is he, bless-ed is he who comes in the name of the Lord.
Optional Choir
E7
Am
f
D
G
C
Ho-san - na, ho-san - na,
Ho - - - san - na
f

ST CLARE ACCLAMATIONS (Holy, Holy, Holy)

Am B7 Em E7 Am D
ho-san-na in the high - est.
Ho-san - na,
in the high - est. Ho - -
G C Am D Em Em
ho-san - na, ho-san-na in the high - est.
-san - na in the high - est.

St Clare Acclamations

We proclaim your Death

Nick Baty

♩ = 104
Priest (Missal chant)
Em B7
The mys - ter - y of faith.
or
♩ = 104
Priest Em C B7
The mys - ter - y of faith.
mf
mf
Em D G
Assembly
We pro-claim your Death, O Lord, and pro-fess your
Am G B7 E
Re - sur - rec - tion un - til you come a - gain.
Optional Choir
Re - sur - rec - tion un - til you come a - gain.

St Clare Acclamations

When we eat this Bread

Nick Baty

♩ = 104
Priest (Missal chant)
Em B7
The mys - ter - y of faith.
or
Priest Em C B7
The mys - ter - y of faith.
mf
Assembly
Em D G
When we eat this Bread and drink this Cup, we pro -
Am G B7 E
claim your Death, O Lord, un-til you come a - gain.
Optional Choir
claim your Death, O Lord, un - til you come a - gain.

St Clare Acclamations

Save us, Saviour of the world

Nick Baty

♩ = 104
Priest (Missal chant)
Em B7
The mys - ter - y of faith.
or
Priest
Em C B7
The mys - ter - y of faith.
mf
Em D G
Assembly
mf Save us, Sa - viour of the world, for by your Cross and
Am G B7 E
Re - sur - rec - tion you have set us free.
optional Choir
Re - sur - rec - tion you have set us free.

St Clare Acclamations

Doxology and Amen

Nick Baty

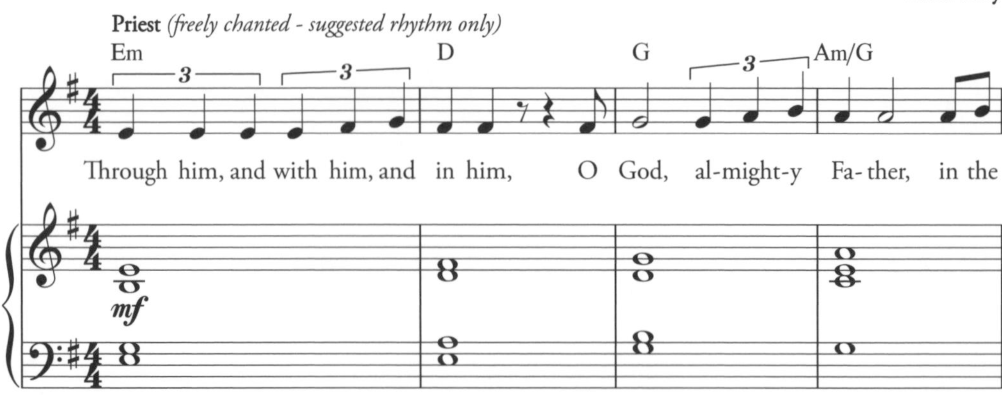

Priest (freely chanted - suggested rhythm only)
Em
D
G
Am/G
Through him, and with him, and in him, O God, al-might-y Fa-ther, in the
mf

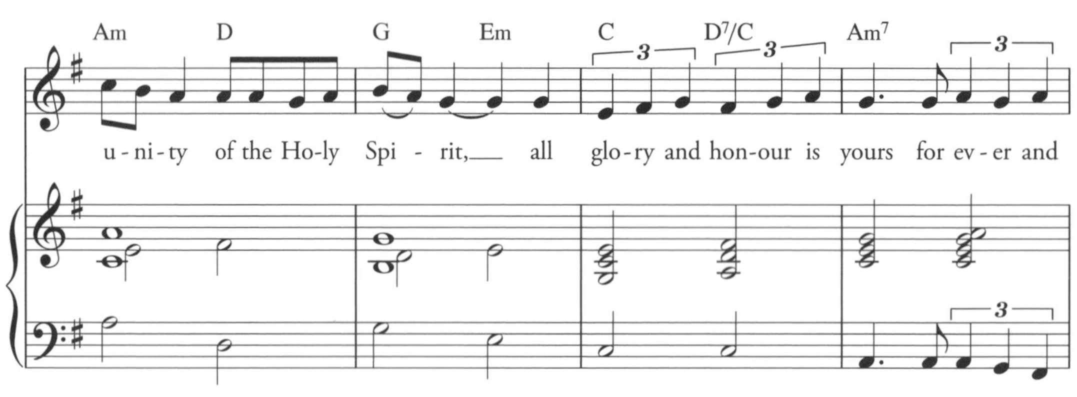

Am
D
G
Em
C
D7/C
Am7
u-ni-ty of the Ho-ly Spi - rit, all glo-ry and hon-our is yours for ev-er and

♩ = 104
E
E7
Am
D
G
C
Am
D
Assembly
ev - er. A - men, a - men, a - -
♩ = 104
f

ST CLARE ACCLAMATIONS (Doxology and Amen)

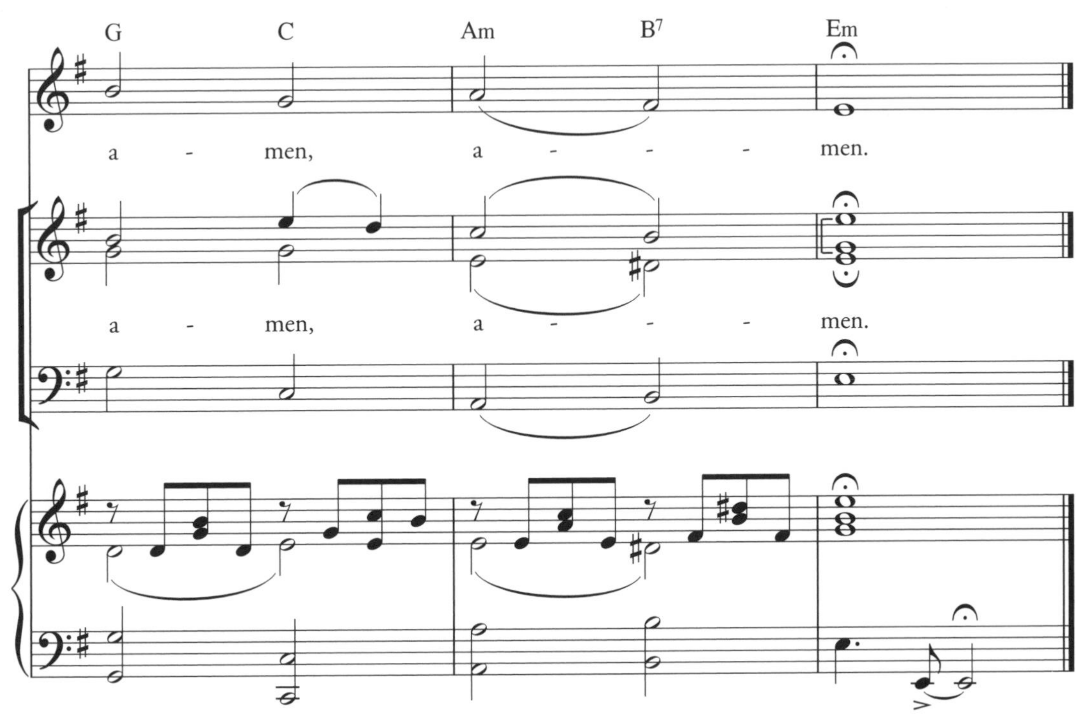

St Clare Acclamations

Doxology and Amen (Missal chant)

Nick Baty

Priest
E
Through him ... ... for ev - er and ev - er.
♩ = 104
Am D G C Am/C D Em E7
Assembly
A - men, a - men, a - men.
♩ = 104
f
3
Am D G C Am B7 Em
A - men, a - men, a - men.
A - men, a - men, a - men.

For Anne Preston and the musicians of Sacred Heart, Warrington

Warrington Acclamations

Holy, Holy, Holy

Nick Baty

♩. = 60
Em D Em D Em D Em Am D
Ho - ly, Ho - ly, Ho - ly___ Lord God of
Piano
mf

E Am D B7 Em Am7 Em Am D
hosts. Heav'n and earth, heav'n and earth are full, are full of your glo - ry. Ho-

Am7 Bm D G B7 Em Am/C Em
san - na,___ ho - san - na,___ ho - san - na
f

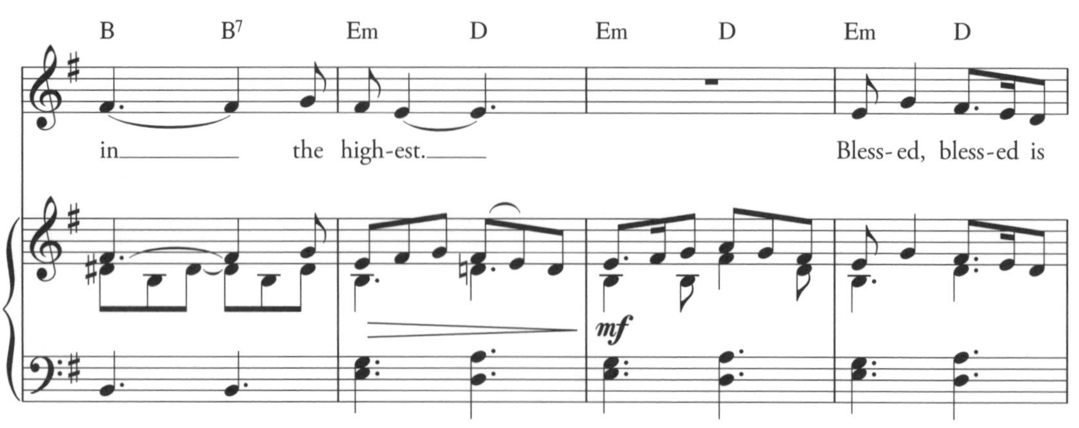
B B7 Em D Em D Em D
in the high-est.
Bless-ed, bless-ed is
mf

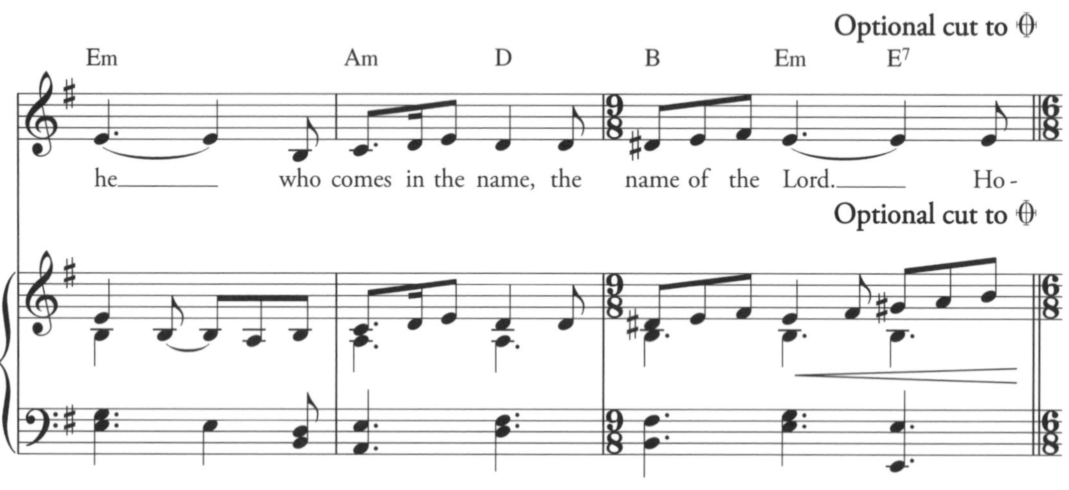
Optional cut to Φ
Em Am D B Em E7
he who comes in the name, the name of the Lord. Ho-
Optional cut to Φ

Am7 Bm D G B7 Em
san - - na, ho-san - - na, ho-
f

Am/C Em B B7 Em E7
san - na in the high-est. Ho-
Optional Choir
Ho - san - na.
Am7 Bm D G B7 Em
san - - na, ho - san - - na, ho-
Ho - san - na. Ho - san - na
Am/C Em B B7 Em D/E Em
san - na in the high-est.
in the high-est.

WARRINGTON ACCLAMATIONS

We proclaim your Death

Nick Baty

♩ = 90
Priest
Em D
The mys - ter-y of faith.
or
♩ = 90
Em D Em D Em D
The mys - t'ry of faith.
mp
mp
Em D C D Em Am D E E7 Am7 Bm
Assembly
We pro-claim your Death, O Lord, and pro - fess your Re-sur - rec-tion un - til you
mf
D G B7 Em Am/C Em B7 Em
come, un - til you come, un - til you come a - gain.

WARRINGTON ACCLAMATIONS

When we eat this Bread

Nick Baty

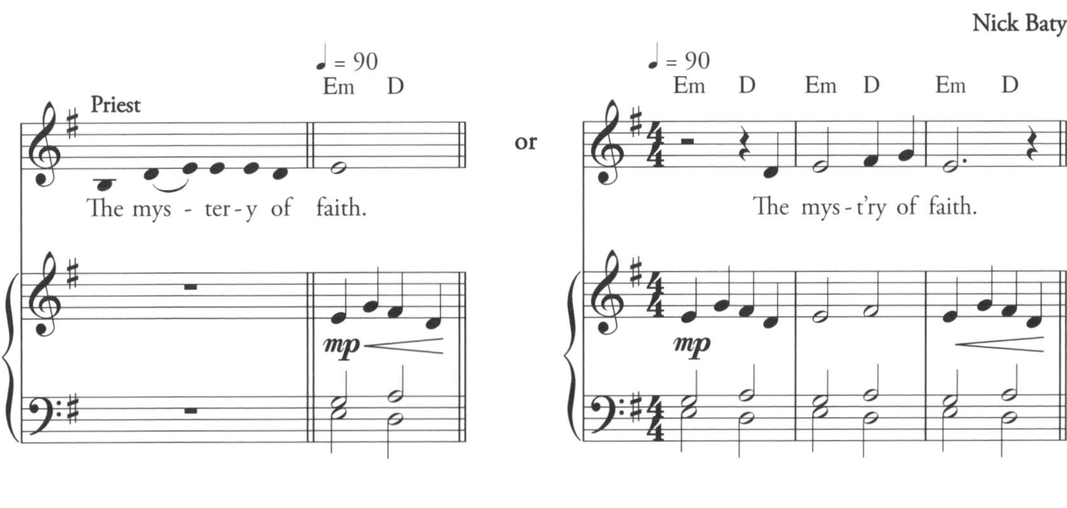
♩ = 90
Em D
Priest
The mys - ter-y of faith.
or
♩ = 90
Em D Em D Em D
The mys-t'ry of faith.
mp
mp

Em D Em D Am D G D Em D
Assembly
When we eat this Bread and drink this Cup, we pro-claim your
mf

Am7 D7 B7 E E7 Am7 Bm D G B7
Death, O Lord, un - til you come, un - til you
3

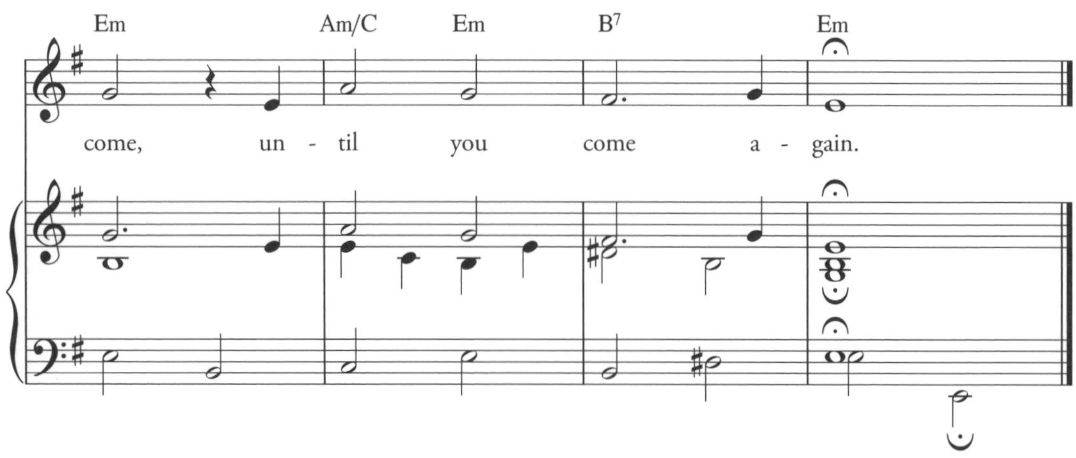
Em Am/C Em B7 Em
come, un - til you come a - gain.

Save us, Saviour of the world.

Nick Baty

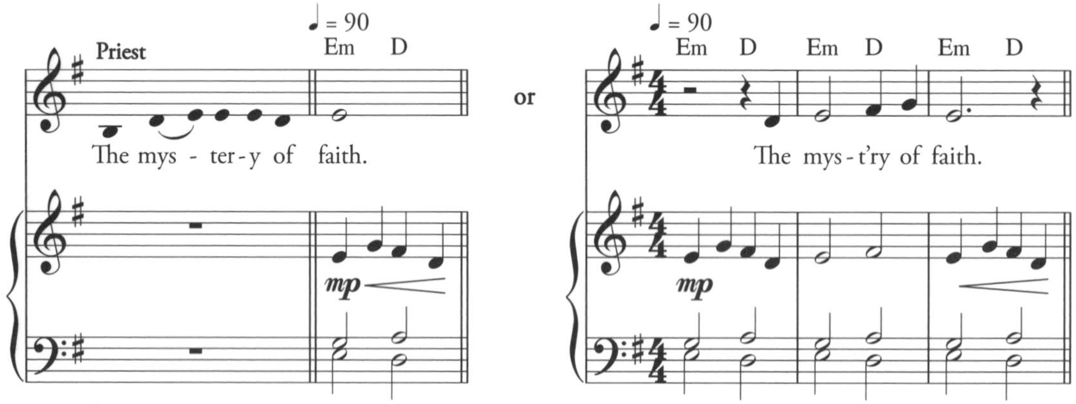

♩ = 90
Priest
Em D
The mys - ter-y of faith.
mp

or

♩ = 90
Em D Em D Em D
The mys-t'ry of faith.
mp

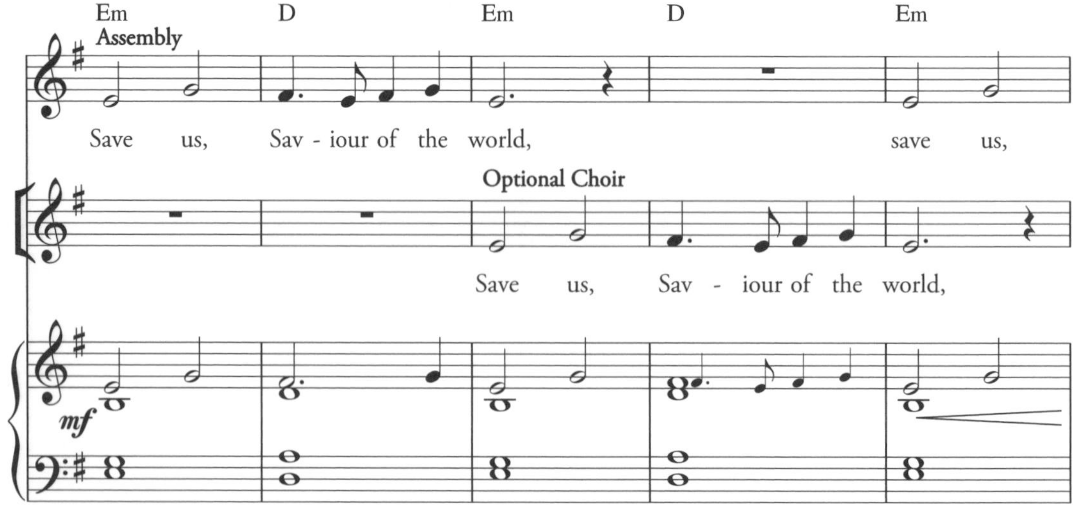

Em D Em D Em
Assembly
Save us, Sav - iour of the world, save us,

Optional Choir
Save us, Sav - iour of the world,
mf

WARRINGTON ACCLAMATIONS

D Em D Am7 Bm D
Sav - iour of the world, for by your Cross and
save us, Sav - iour of the world, for by your
3
f
G B7 Em Am/C Em B7
Re - sur - rec - tion you have set us
Cross and Re - sur - rec - tion, save us.
3
Em D E
free.
Save us, Sa - viour of the world.

Doxology and Amen

Nick Baty

Priest *(Either sing this Missal tone...)* ♩. = 60 Go to ⊕

Through him ... ... for ev - er___ and ev - ver.

Em E Go to ⊕

mf

Slightly slower than the *Holy*

Em D Em Am D E

Priest *(...or this setting)*

Through him, and with him, and in him,_ O God, al-might-y Fa-ther,___ in the

Slightly slower than the *Holy*

mp

Am D B7 Em Am D
u - ni - ty of the Ho - ly Spi - rit,___ all glo - ry___ and

C Em Am D B7 accel. E7
ho - nour is yours, for ev - er and ev - er.
accel.
Am7 Bm D G B7 Em
Assembly
A - - men, a - - men,
Optional Choir
A - - men, a - -
(♩. = 60)
f
Am/C Em B7 Em D/E Em
a - - men, a - men.
-men, a - men, a - men.

Lord, have mercy

Peter Jones

♩ = c.66
1st time: Cantor, 2nd: Assembly
simile
Lord,___ have mer - cy. Christ,_ have
Or: Ky - ri - e, e - lei - son. Chris - te, e -
Organ
p legato
simile
mer - cy. Lord,___ have mer - cy.
lei - son. Ky - ri - e, e - lei - son.
pp

Lord, have mercy

Alan Smith

LORD, HAVE MERCY (Alan Smith)

LORD, HAVE MERCY (Alan Smith)

G
Dm
mer - cy.
Christ,
have
B7
C
mer - cy.
Christ,
have

LORD, HAVE MERCY (Alan Smith)

LORD, HAVE MERCY (Alan Smith)

G
mer - cy.
Lord, have
F
mer - cy.
Lord, have

LORD, HAVE MERCY (Alan Smith)

Glory to God

Peter Jones

Steady ♩ = 88
2nd time only
Assembly
Glo-ry to God,
mf
Cantor/Choir
Glo-ry to God,
mf
Steady ♩ = 88
Organ
mf
mf
1.
glo-ry in the high - est, and on earth peace to
glo-ry in the high - est, and on earth peace to peo-ple of good will.
1.

2.
peo-ple of good will.
Glo-ry in the high - est.
peo-ple of good will. We praise you, we bless you,
2.

Glo-ry in the high - est.
mp
we a-dore you,
we glo-ri-fy you, we give you
mp
mp

GLORY TO GOD (Peter Jones)

Glo-ry in the high - est.
thanks for your great glo - ry, Lord God,
heav'n-ly King,
f
mf

Glo-ry in the high - est.
Glo-ry to God,
Cantor: small notes *ad lib.*
O God, al-might-y Fa - ther.
Glo-ry to God,
mf

GLORY TO GOD (Peter Jones)

glo - ry in the high - est, and on earth peace to peo-ple of good will.
glo - ry in the high - est, and on earth peace to peo-ple of good will.

mp
Lord Je-sus Christ, On-ly Be-got-ten Son, Lord God, Lamb of God, Son of the Fa - ther,
mp
mp legato

GLORY TO GOD (Peter Jones)

have mer - cy on us;
mf
you take a-way the sins of the world, have mer - cy on us, have mer - cy on us;
mf
mf
re - ceive our prayer;
mp
(Cantor)
mf
you take a-way the sins of the world, re - ceive our prayer, re - ceive our prayer; you are
you take a-way the sins of the world, re - ceive our prayer, re - ceive our prayer; you are
mp
mf
mp
mf

GLORY TO GOD (Peter Jones)

have mer-cy on us.
seat-ed at the right hand of the Fa-ther, have mer-cy on us, have mer-cy on us.

2nd time only
Glo-ry to God, glo-ry in the high - est,
mf
Glo-ry to God, glo-ry in the high - est,
mf
mf
mf

GLORY TO GOD (Peter Jones)

1.
2.
and on earth peace to
peo-ple of good will.
and on earth peace to peo-ple of good will.
peo-ple of good will.

p
mf
For you a-lone are the Ho - ly One, you a - lone are the Lord, you a -

GLORY TO GOD (Peter Jones)

lone are the Most High, Je - sus Christ, with the Ho - ly Spi - rit,

Cantor: small notes *ad lib.*
in the glo - ry of God, the glo - ry of God the Fa - ther.

GLORY TO GOD (Peter Jones)

Glo-ry to God, glo-ry in the high - est, and on earth peace to
f
Glo-ry to God, glo-ry in the high - est, and on earth peace to
f
f
peo-ple of good will. A - men.
rit.
ff
fff
peo-ple of good will. A - men. A - men.
ff
fff
rit.
Trpt.
fff

Glory to God

David Saint

Joyful ♩ = c.120
REFRAIN: 1st time - Cantors, 2nd - Assembly
mf Glo - ri - a, glo - ri - a in ex - cel - sis De - o.
Glo - ri - a, glo - ri - a in ex - cel - sis De - o. De - o.
1.
2. To verses
Last time
De - o.
Cantors
A - - men.
Assembly
A - - men.
Fine
VERSE 1: Cantors/Choir
Glory to God in the highest, and on earth peace to people of good will.
D.C.
VERSE 2: Cantors/Choir
We praise you, we bless you, we a - dore you, we glorify you,

D.C.
we give you thanks for your great glory, Lord God, heaven-ly King, O God, almight-y Father.
VERSE 3: Cantors/Choir
Lord Je - sus Christ, Only Begotten Son, Lord God, Lamb of God, Son of the Father,
you take away the sins of the world, have mercy on us; you take away the sins of the world,
D.C.
receive our prayer; you are seated at the right hand of the Father, have mercy on us.
VERSE 4: Cantors/Choir
For you alone are the Ho - ly One, you alone are the Lord,
D.C.
you alone are the Most High, Jesus Christ, with the Holy Spirit, in the glory of God the Father.

Glory to God

Peter Roberts

Em ♩. = 65
Bm7
Cadd2
D
mf Glo-ry to God in the high-est, and on earth peace to peo-ple of good
f Glo-ry to God in the high-est, and on earth peace to peo-ple of good
Optional repeat - 1st time: Cantor/Choir; 2nd: All
mf (f)
Em Bm/E
1. Em
2. Em
Cantor
A
Em
will.
will.
We praise you, we bless you, we a-
mf
A
Em
Cadd2
Dadd2
A
dore you, we glo-ri-fy you, we give you thanks for your great glo-ry,

GLORY TO GOD (Peter Roberts)

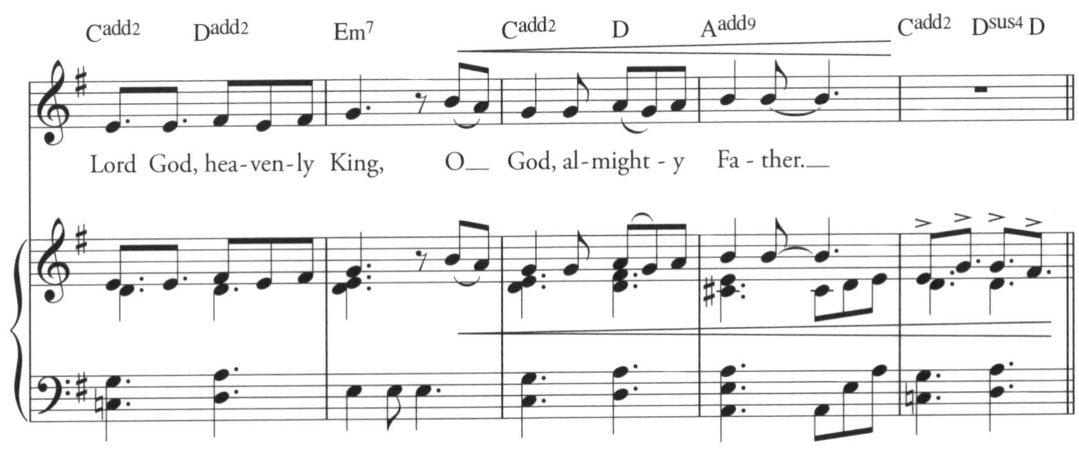
Cadd2 Dadd2 Em7 Cadd2 D Aadd9 Cadd2 Dsus4 D
Lord God, hea-ven-ly King, O__ God, al-might-y Fa-ther.__

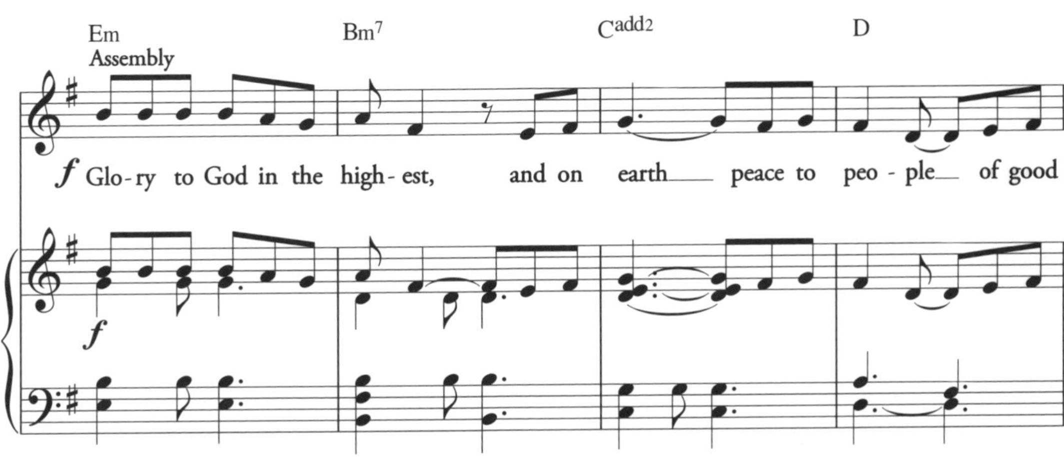
Em Bm7 Cadd2 D
Assembly
f Glo-ry to God in the high-est, and on earth__ peace to peo-ple__ of good
f

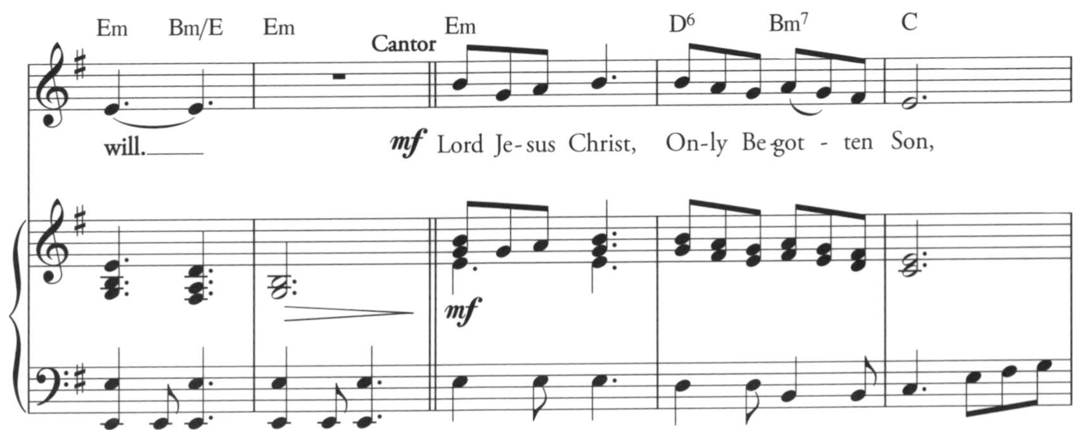
Em Bm/E Em Em D6 Bm7 C
Cantor
will.__ mf Lord Je-sus Christ, On-ly Be-got-ten Son,
mf

GLORY TO GOD (Peter Roberts)

Am
C6
D6
Em
A
Lord God, Lamb of God, Son of the Fa - ther,
you take a - way the sins of the
C
Am
D
Em
A
C
world, have mer-cy on us;
you take a - way the sins of the world, re-
Am
D
Em
Cmaj7
D
A
ceive our prayer;
you are seat-ed at the right hand of the Fa - ther,
C
D6
Assembly
Em
Bm7
have mer-cy on us.
f Glo-ry to God in the high-est, and on

GLORY TO GOD (Peter Roberts)

Cadd2
D
Em
Bm/E
Em
Cantor
A
earth peace to peo-ple of good will.
mf
For you a-lone are the
mf

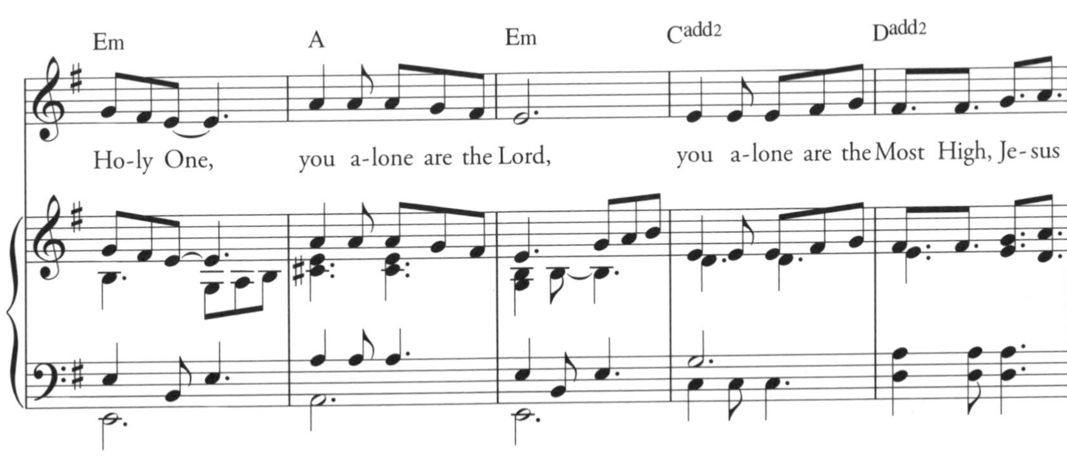
Em
A
Em
Cadd2
Dadd2
Ho-ly One, you a-lone are the Lord, you a-lone are the Most High, Je-sus

Aadd9
Cadd2
Dadd2
Em7
Cadd2
D
Aadd9
Christ, with the Ho - ly Spi-rit, in the glo-ry of God the Fa - ther.

GLORY TO GOD (Peter Roberts)

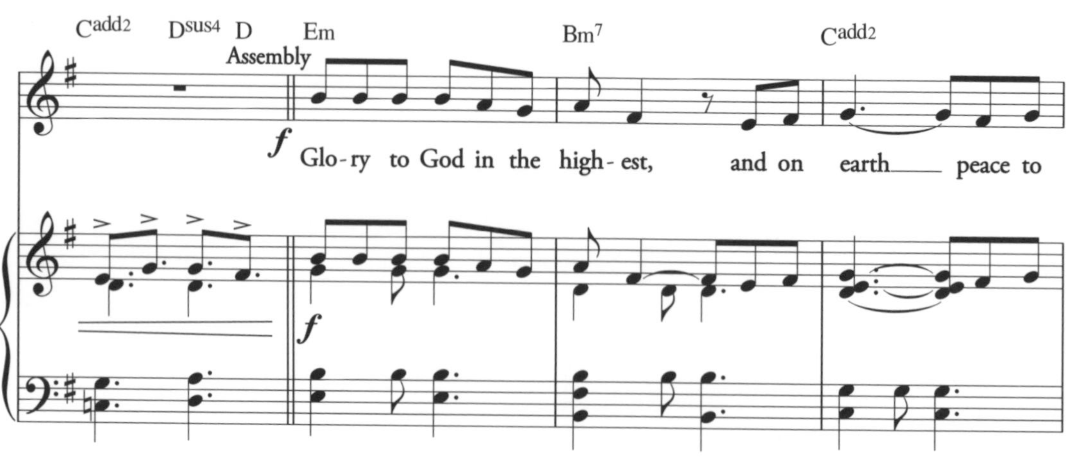
Cadd2 Dsus4 D Em Bm7 Cadd2
Assembly
f
Glo-ry to God in the high-est, and on earth peace to
f

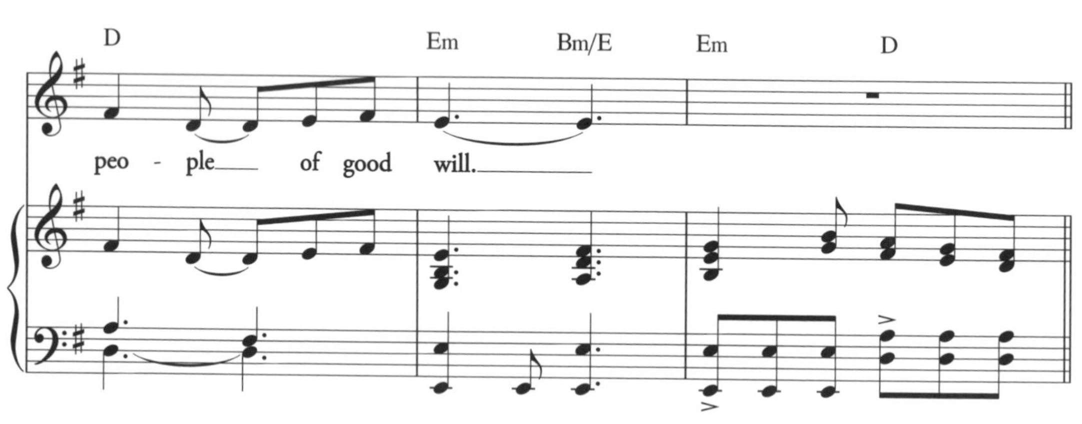
D Em Bm/E Em D
peo - ple of good will.

Cadd2 Bm7 Aadd9 rit. Cadd2 D E
ff
più f A - - men. A - - men.
rit.
più f
ff

Aston Gospel Acclamation

Peter Jones

Allegro ♩ = c.132
1st time: Cantor(s), 2nd: Assembly
Em Bm Em N.C. Em Bm Em D C B E
Al - le - lu - ia, al - le - lu - ia,
Organ
mf

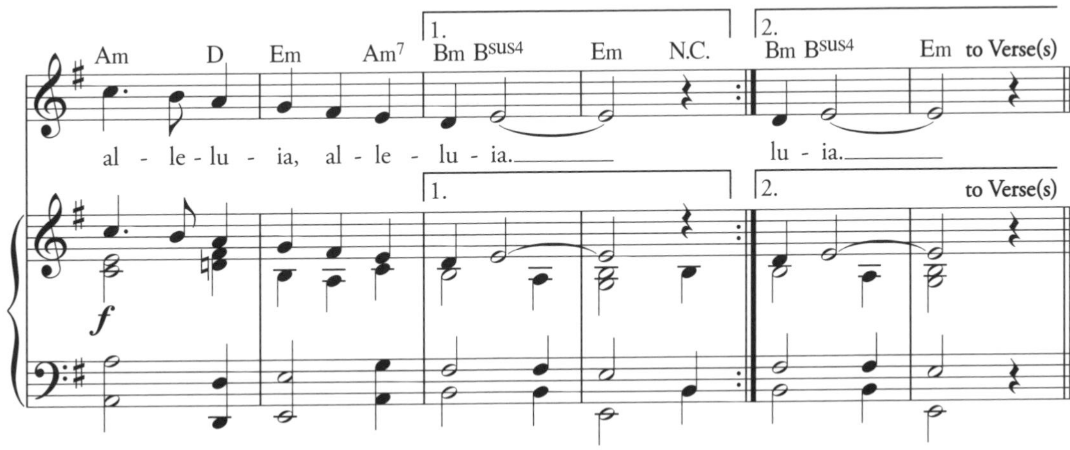
Am D Em Am7 Bm Bsus4 Em N.C. Bm Bsus4 Em to Verse(s)
1.
2.
al - le - lu - ia, al - le - lu - ia.
lu - ia.
to Verse(s)
f

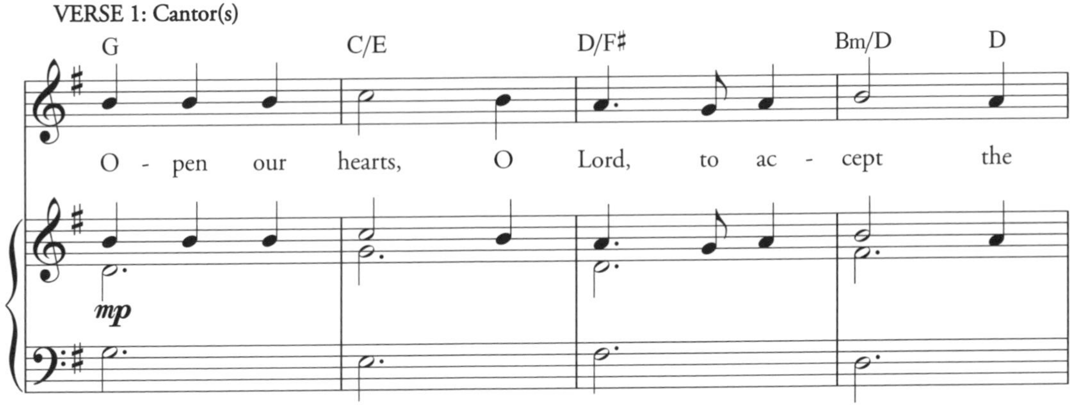
VERSE 1: Cantor(s)
G C/E D/F♯ Bm/D D
O - pen our hearts, O Lord, to ac - cept the
mp

Verses from Revised Edition of *The Roman Lectionary* for the dioceses of England, Wales, Scotland and Ireland, 1981.

ASTON GOSPEL ACCLAMATION (Peter Jones)

Em C D B B7 To ⊕
words of your Son.
To ⊕
VERSE 2: Cantor(s)
G C/E D/F♯ Bm
Speak, Lord, your ser - vant is lis - ten - ing, you have the
mp
Em Em/D C G/B Am Am6/C B To ⊕
mes - sage of e - ter - nal life.
To ⊕
VERSE 3: Cantor(s)
G C/E D/F♯ Bm
Your word is truth, O Lord, con - se -
mp

ASTON GOSPEL ACCLAMATION (Peter Jones)

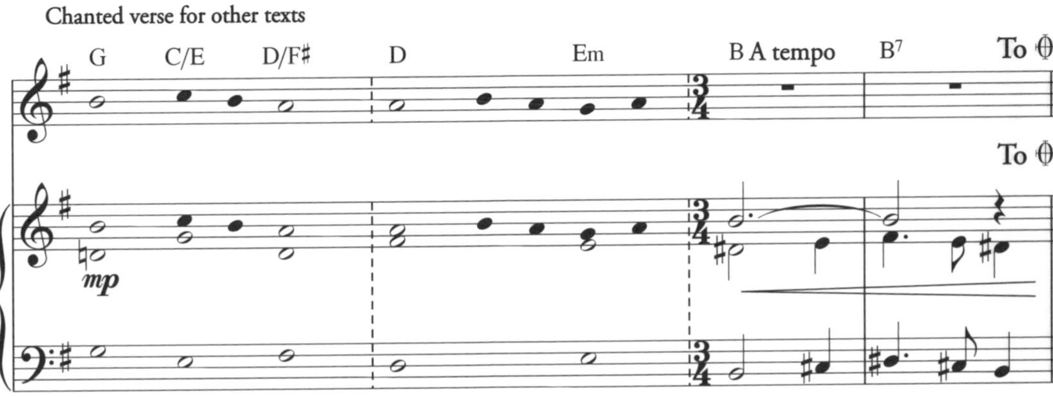

Aston Lenten Gospel Acclamation

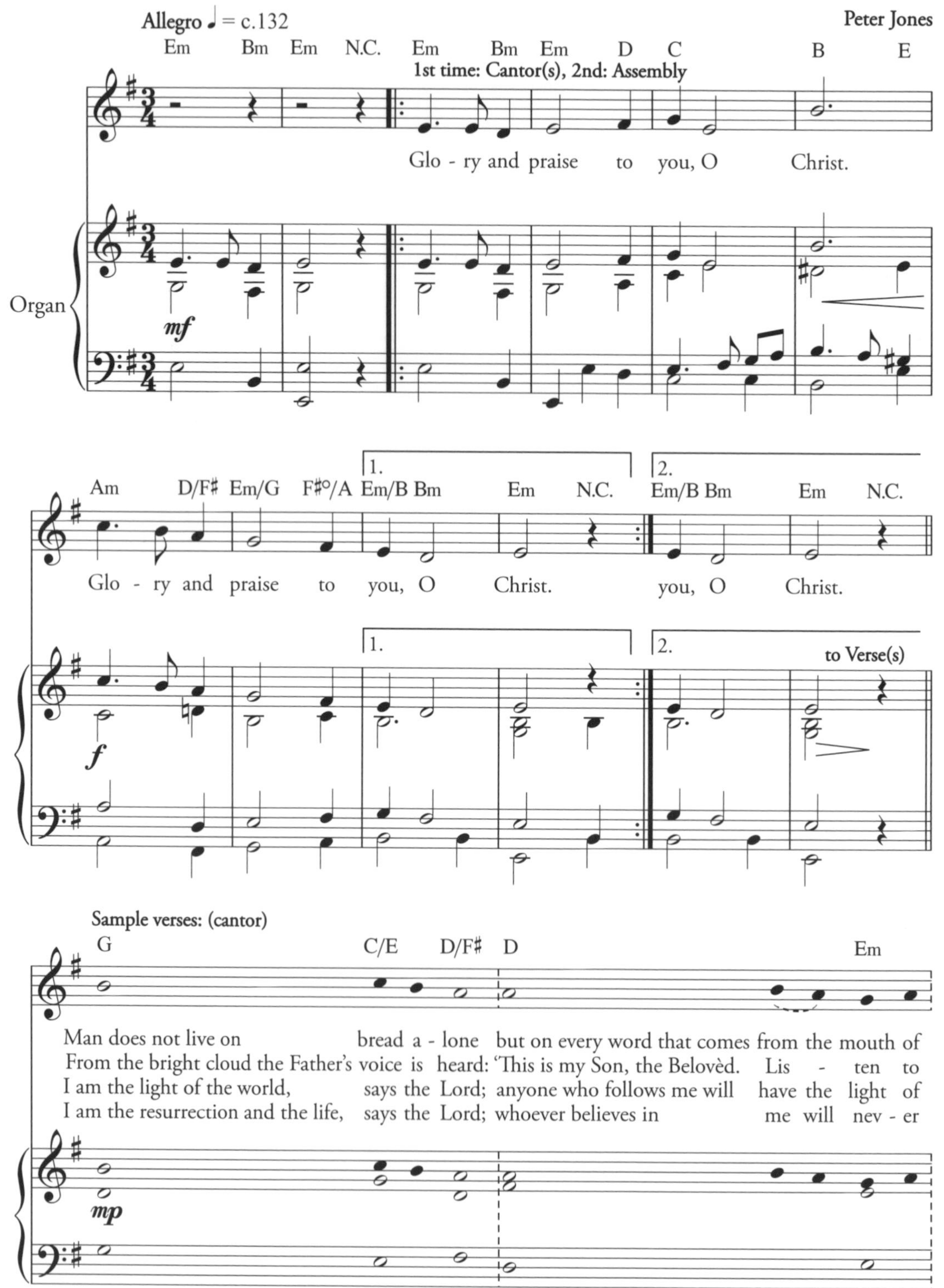
Allegro ♩ = c.132
Peter Jones
Em Bm Em N.C. Em Bm Em D C B E
1st time: Cantor(s), 2nd: Assembly
Glo - ry and praise to you, O Christ.
Organ
mf
Am D/F♯ Em/G F♯°/A Em/B Bm Em N.C. Em/B Bm Em N.C.
1.
2.
Glo - ry and praise to you, O Christ. you, O Christ.
to Verse(s)
f
Sample verses: (cantor)
G C/E D/F♯ D Em
Man does not live on bread a - lone but on every word that comes from the mouth of
From the bright cloud the Father's voice is heard: 'This is my Son, the Belovèd. Lis - ten to
I am the light of the world, says the Lord; anyone who follows me will have the light of
I am the resurrection and the life, says the Lord; whoever believes in me will nev - er
mp

Verses from Revised Edition of *The Roman Lectionary* for the dioceses of England, Wales, Scotland and Ireland, 1981.

ASTON LENTEN GOSPEL ACCLAMATION (Peter Jones)

A tempo
B
B7
Assembly
Em
Bm
Em
D
C
B
E
God.
him.
life.
die.
Glo - ry and praise to you, O Christ.
f
Am
D/F♯
Em/G
F♯°/A
Em
Bm
E
rit.
Glo - ry and praise to you, O Christ.
f
rit.

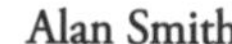

Festal Gospel Acclamation

Alan Smith

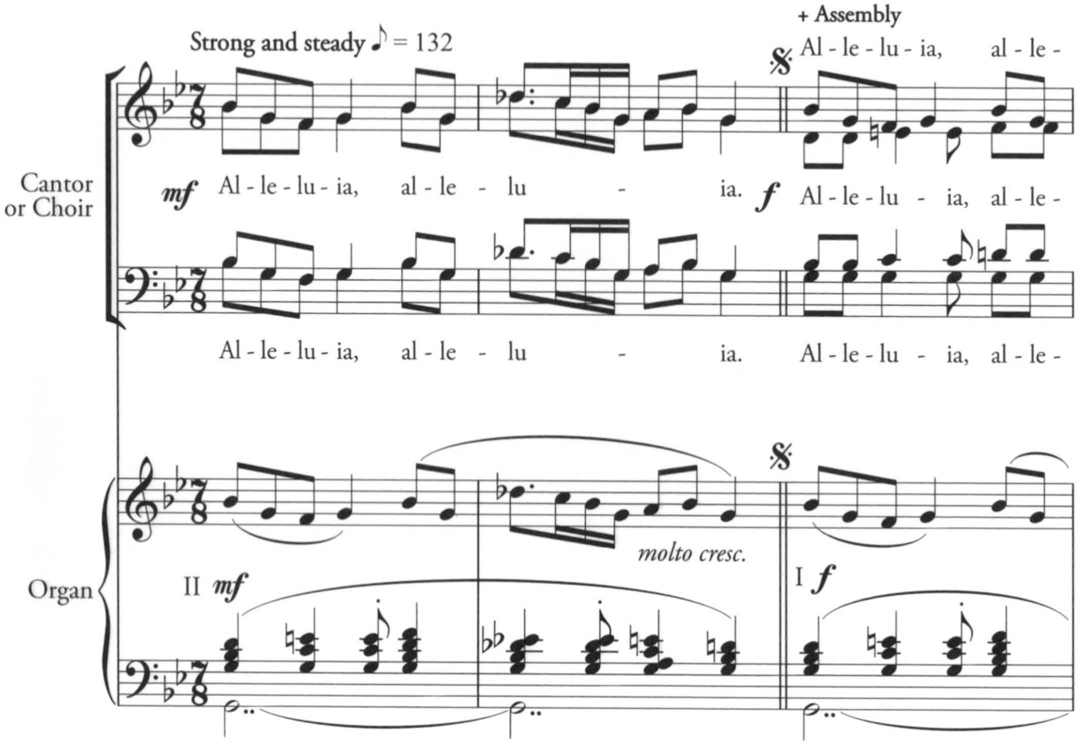
Strong and steady ♪ = 132
+ Assembly
Al - le - lu - ia, al - le -
Cantor or Choir
mf Al - le - lu - ia, al - le - lu - ia.
f Al - le - lu - ia, al - le -
Al - le - lu - ia, al - le - lu - ia. Al - le - lu - ia, al - le -
Organ
molto cresc.
II mf
I f

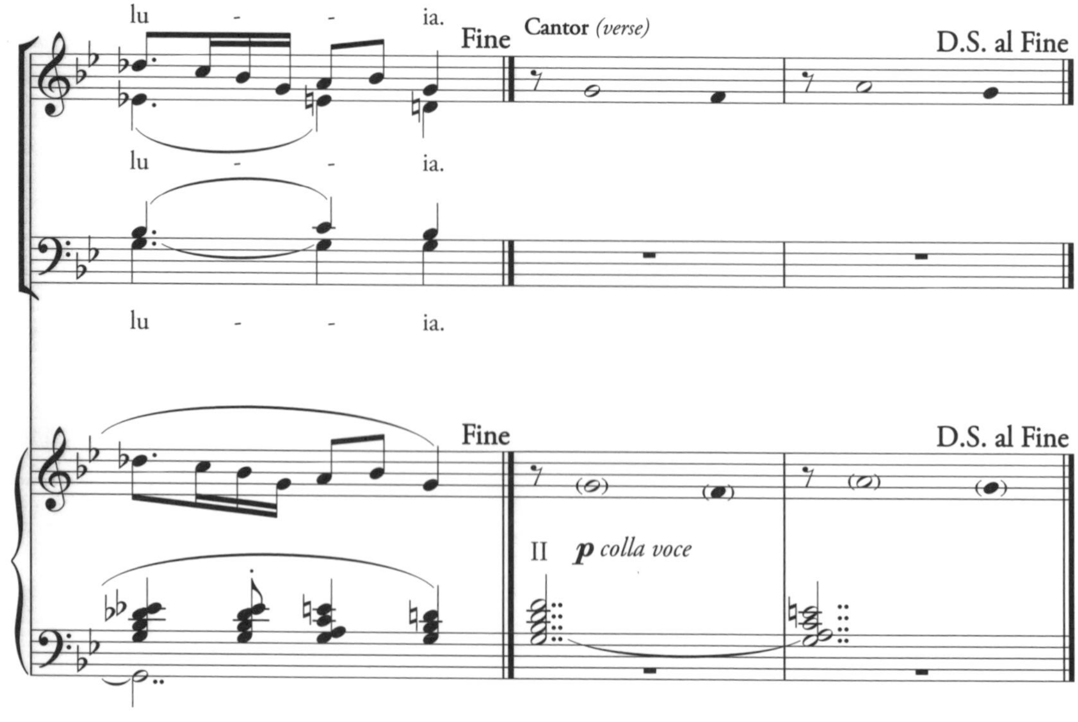
lu - - ia.
Fine
Cantor (verse)
D.S. al Fine
lu - - ia.
lu - - ia.
Fine
D.S. al Fine
II p colla voce

Gospel Greeting

Peter Jones

Flowing ♩ = c.50
Cantor
Al - le - lu - ia. Al - le-
Organ
mp
lu - ia, Al - le - lu - ia.
Assembly
Al - le - lu - ia. Al - le-
mf
1.
Final
Fine
lu - ia. Al - le - lu - ia.
lu - ia.

Verses from Revised Edition of *The Roman Lectionary* for the dioceses of England, Wales, Scotland and Ireland, 1981.

GOSPEL GREETING (Peter Jones)

VERSE 1: Cantor
I am the light of the world says the Lord,
mp

D.C. al Fine
an - y - one who fol - lows me will have the light of life.
D.C. al Fine

VERSE 2: Cantor
I am the good shep - herd, says the Lord;
mp

GOSPEL GREETING (Peter Jones)

D.C. al Fine
I know my own sheep and my own__ know me.
D.C. al Fine

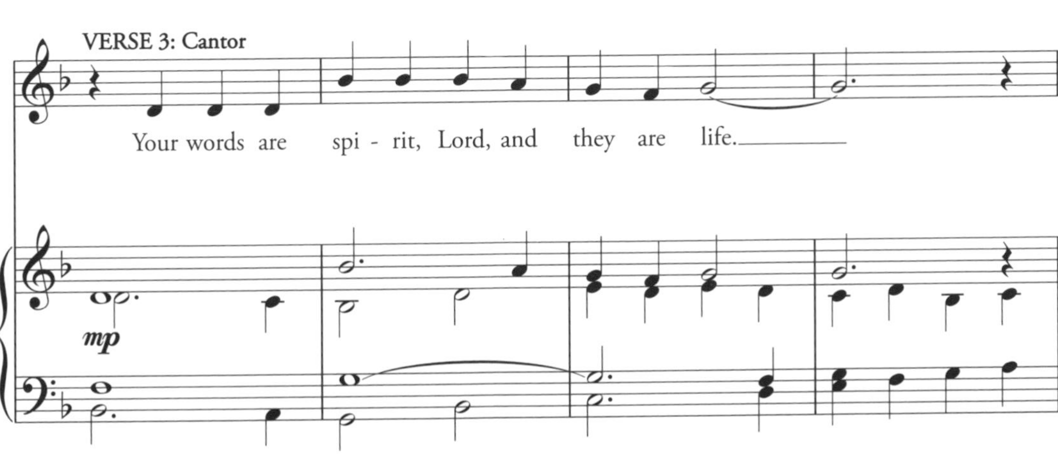
VERSE 3: Cantor
Your words are spi - rit, Lord, and they are life.
mp

D.C. al Fine
You have the mes - sage of e - ter - nal life.
D.C. al Fine

Resurrection Gospel Acclamation

Stephen Dean

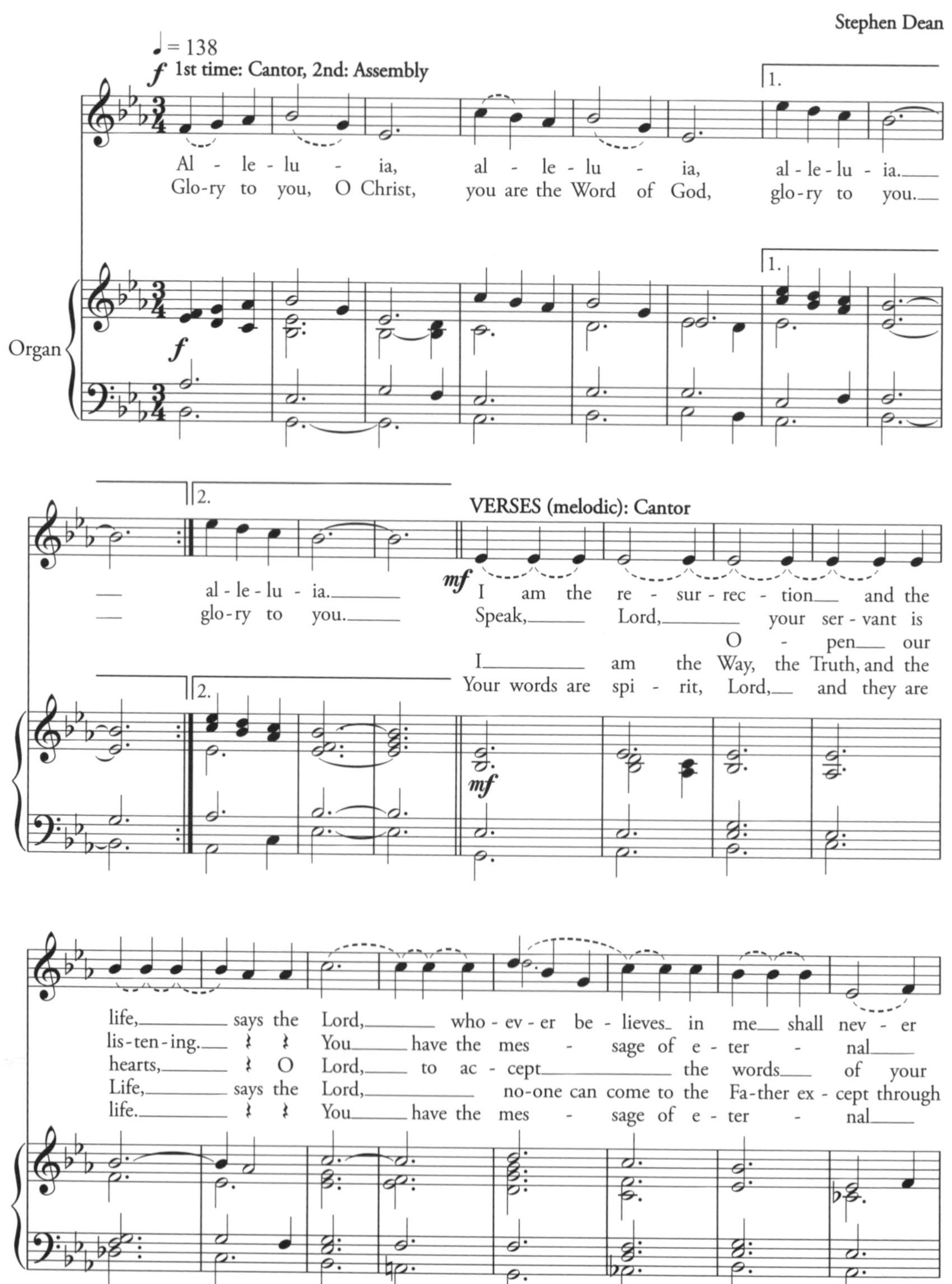
♩= 138
f 1st time: Cantor, 2nd: Assembly
1.
Al - le - lu - ia, al - le - lu - ia, al - le - lu - ia.
Glo-ry to you, O Christ, you are the Word of God, glo-ry to you.
Organ
2.
al - le - lu - ia.
glo-ry to you.
VERSES (melodic): Cantor
mf
I am the re - sur - rec - tion and the life, says the Lord, who - ev - er be - lieves in me shall nev - er
Speak, Lord, your ser - vant is lis-ten-ing. You have the mes - sage of e - ter - nal
O - pen our hearts, O Lord, to ac - cept the words of your
I am the Way, the Truth, and the Life, says the Lord, no-one can come to the Fa-ther ex - cept through
Your words are spi - rit, Lord, and they are life. You have the mes - sage of e - ter - nal

Verses from Revised Edition of *The Roman Lectionary* for the dioceses of England, Wales, Scotland and Ireland, 1981.

RESURRECTION GOSPEL ACCLAMATION (Stephen Dean)

to final refrain
die.
life.
Son.
me.
life.
VERSES (psalm tone): Cantor
Blessed are you, Father, Lord of heaven and earth, for re-
Your words are spirit, Lord, and they are life;
mf
vealing the mysteries of the kingdom to mere chil - dren.
you have the message of e - ter - nal life.
to final refrain
Assembly
Al - le - lu - ia, al - le - lu - ia, al - le - lu - ia.
Glo - ry to you, O Christ, you are the Word of God, glo - ry to you.
Fine
Fine

St Agatha Alleluia

Martin Barry

Joyfully ♩. = 60
D
G
Em
Asus4
A
Assembly & Cantor/Choir
Organ
mf

1st time: Cantor/Choir only
D
G
Em Asus4 A
D
G
Al - le - lu - ia, al - le - lu - ia. Al - le - lu - ia, al -
Al - le - lu - ia, al - le - lu - ia. Al - le - lu - ia,
Al - le - lu - ia. Al - le -
Al - le - lu - ia, al - le - lu - ia. Al - le - lu - ia, al -
f

Verses from Revised Edition of *The Roman Lectionary* for the dioceses of England, Wales, Scotland and Ireland, 1981.

ST AGATHA ALLELUIA (Martin Barry)

Em Asus4 A D A D E
le - lu - ia. Al - le - lu - ia, al - le - lu -
al - le - lu - ia. Al - le lu - ia, al - le - lu -
lu - ia. Al - le - lu - ia, al - le - lu -
le - lu - ia. Al - le - lu - ia, al - le - lu -

A D G Em Asus4 A D
ia. Al - le - lu - ia, al - le - lu - ia!
Fine
ia. Al - le - lu - ia, al - le - lu - ia!
ia. Al - le - lu - ia.!
ia. Al - le - lu - ia, al - le - lu - ia!
Fine

ST AGATHA ALLELUIA (Martin Barry)

C/D
D
C/D
D
mf Cantor/Choir
O - pen our hearts, O Lord, to ac -
mf
mf

G
Em
Asus4
A
D.S. al Fine
cept the words of your Son.
D.S. al Fine

Aston Lamb of God

Peter Jones

Flowing ♩ = c.80
G D G D Em Bm
Lamb of God, you take a-way the
Piano
p legato
C G Am D G D
sins of the world, have mer - cy on us. Lamb of God,
rit.
Em Bm C G Am/D D Am7/D D G
you take a-way the sins of the world, grant us peace.
rit.

In Pace Lamb of God

Christopher Walker

♩ = c.120
Cantor
Lamb of God, you take_ a - way_ the sins of the world, have mer-cy on us,
Assembly
have mer-cy on us.
Organ
Repeat as necessary
Final
world,
Cantor
grant us peace,
rall. e dim.
Assembly
grant us peace._
rit.

Lamb of God

Martin Barry

Tranquil ♩ = 80
Flute
Assembly & SA
TB
Piano
A
F♯m
Bm
E
mp
Lamb of God, you take a - way the sins of the world, have mer - cy, have
A
F♯m
Bm
Esus4
E
A

LAMB OF GOD (Martin Barry)

mer - cy on us.
Lamb of God, you take a - way the
D
Bm7
E
A
F#m
sins of the world, have mer - cy, have mer - cy on us.
Bm
Esus4
E
A
D
Bm7

LAMB OF GOD (Martin Barry)

Lamb of God, you take a - way the
E
A
E/G♯
F♯m
C♯m
poco rit.
A tempo
sins of the world, grant us, grant us peace.
poco rit.
A tempo
D
G9
A
F♯m
E7
A

Lamb of God

Peter Jones

𝅗𝅥 = 55
Cantor/Choir
p legato
Lamb of God, you take a-way the
Organ
p legato
sins of the world, have mer - cy on us.
Assembly
Have mer - cy on
mf
us.
Cantor/Choir
Lamb of God, you take a-way the sins of the world,
mp

LAMB OF GOD (Peter Jones)

Assembly
Cantor/Choir
— have mer - cy on us. Have mer - cy on us. Lamb of
mp
mf
p
God, you take a - way the sins of the world,
Assembly
— grant us peace. Grant us peace.
mp

Saint Joseph's Lamb of God

Alan Smith

Gently moving
p
Lamb of God, you take a-way the sins of the world, have mer-cy on us.
Organ
p legato
Lamb of God, you take a-way the sins of the world, have mer-cy on us.
p
Lamb of God, you take a-way the sins of the world, grant us peace.
rit.
rit.
p

Instrumental Parts

The following instrumental parts are available in PDF format on request from the publisher:

Mass of St Luke (Mike Stanley)
C instrument 1
C instrument 2
C instrument 3
B♭ instrument 1
B♭ instrument 2
B♭ instrument 3

Pershore Mass (Alan Smith)
2 trumpets in B♭
2 trombones
3 timpani

Saint Chad's Acclamations (Peter Jones)
2 trumpets in B♭
2 trombones
3 timpani

St Clare Acclamations (Nick Baty)
flute
clarinet in B♭

Warrington Acclamations (Nick Baty)
flute

Lord, have mercy (Alan Smith)
flute
guitar

Glory to God (Peter Jones)
3 trumpets in B♭
3 trombones
4 timpani

Glory to God (Peter Roberts)
flute
trumpet in B♭
violin
cello

Lamb of God (Martin Barry)
flute